# Connected Mathematics 2™

# Assessment Resources

# Grade 7

Glenda Lappan
James T. Fey
William M. Fitzgerald
Susan Friel
Elizabeth Difanis Phillips

D1299786

PEARSON

Boston, Massachusetts • Glenview, Illinois • Shoreview, Minnesota • Upper Saddle River, New Jersey

*Connected Mathematics*™ Project was developed at Michigan State University with financial support from the Michigan State University Office of the Provost, Computing and Technology, and the College of Natural Science.

 *Connected Mathematics*™ is based upon work supported by the National Science Foundation under Grant No. MDR 9150217 and Grant No. ESI 9986372. Opinions expressed are those of the authors and not necessarily those of the Foundation.

The Michigan State University authors and administration have agreed that all MSU royalties arising from this publication will be devoted to purposes supported by the Department of Mathematics and the MSU Mathematics Enrichment Fund.

**Acknowledgments** The people who made up the *Connected Mathematics 2* team—representing editorial, editorial services, design services, and production services—are listed below. Bold type denotes core team members.

Leora Adler, Judith Buice, Kerry Cashman, Patrick Culleton, Sheila DeFazio, Katie Hallahan, Richard Heater, **Barbara Holllingdale, Jayne Holman,** Karen Holtzman, **Etta Jacobs,** Christine Lee, Carolyn Lock, Catherine Maglio, **Dotti Marshall,** Rich McMahon, Eve Melnechuk, Terri Mitchell, **Marsha Novak,** Irene Rubin, Donna Russo, Robin Samper, Siri Schwartzman, **Nancy Smith,** Emily Soltanoff, **Mark Tricca,** Paula Vergith, Roberta Warshaw, Helen Young.

13-digit ISBN 978-0-13-366126-2
10-digit ISBN 0-13-366126-1
1 2 3 4 5 6 7 8 9 10   11 10 09 08 07

# Table of Contents

## Introduction

A rubric is a scoring tool that lists the criteria for scoring a solution to a problem. Most often, rubrics show the level of performance expected for several levels of quality, which may be recorded as points or comments. Correct answers alone do not necessarily imply understanding of the mathematical concepts. It is assumed throughout the curriculum that students should be in the habit of providing evidence of their reasoning and understanding. In the sample rubrics provided in this section, you will see that many points are assigned specifically to student explanations.

When writing a rubric, you should take into consideration the goals of the assessment. Some rubrics also specify the level of assistance from the teacher or the aide in the classroom. For example, more points may be awarded for a student's independent performance rather than with assistance.

Part of the assessment process when using a rubric is the teacher's reflection on the student's understanding of the concepts. In addition to a numerical score, or grade, the teacher should consider the difference between careless errors and errors due to a student's incorrect understanding of a concept. The teacher's comments for the samples in this section provide a model of the conclusions you should draw from your students' work.

Students should be aware of the evaluation criteria for their assessments. Since a rubric can help the student understand what a quality answer should be, it is often valuable to share the rubric with the student before the student begins the assessment.

The Partner Quizzes in this booklet are intended for students to take in pairs, working together with access to notebooks, calculators, and other appropriate materials. These questions are generally more open-ended than those found on other assessments. Students should be permitted to submit a draft to the teacher for input, and then have an opportunity to revise their work, before turning in their final responses. Even more attention should be given to evidence of mathematical reasoning when assessing a Partner Quiz.

This booklet includes a general scoring rubric that you can use for any question, as well as sample rubrics, sample work, and teacher comments for the *Variables and Patterns Unit Test.* Note that before *Moving Straight Ahead,* the terms *slope* and *y-intercept* have not been introduced. In *Variables and Patterns,* for example, most students will write their rule in the form $y = b + mx$, and will refer to the *y*-intercept as the starting point.

## General Scoring Rubric

A suggested scoring rubric is described below. Teachers may use this guide to award the same number of possible points for each question based on the completeness of the answer.

This rubric awards a maximum of 3 points for each question, based on the general guidelines given.

### 3: COMPLETE RESPONSE

- Complete, with clear, coherent explanations
- Shows understanding of the mathematical concepts and procedures
- Satisfies all essential conditions of the problem

### 2: REASONABLY COMPLETE RESPONSE

- Reasonably complete; may lack detail in explanation
- Shows understanding of most of the mathematical concepts and procedures
- Satisfies most of the essential conditions of the problem

### 1: PARTIAL RESPONSE

- Incomplete; explanation is insufficient or not understandable
- Shows little understanding of the mathematical concepts and procedures
- Fails to address essential conditions of the problem

### 0: NO ATTEMPT

- Irrelevant response
- Does not attempt a solution
- Does not address conditions of the problem

# Variables and Patterns Unit Test

The final assessment for *Variables and Patterns* is a unit test. Below is a suggested scoring rubric and a grading scale for the unit test. They are followed by samples of student work and a teacher's comments on each sample.

## Suggested Scoring Rubric

This rubric uses a scale with a total of 50 possible points. You may use the rubric as presented here or modify it to fit your district's requirements for evaluating and reporting students' work and understanding. CMP students should be in the habit of providing evidence for the reasoning for each answer.

As you review the rubric and the student work, note that students are not penalized twice for an error. If a student derives a value that is needed to find another solution, and that value is incorrect, and then carries out a correct procedure with the incorrect value, he or she is given credit for the correct procedure.

### QUESTION 1: 14 POINTS

- 6 points for a correct table with a title, labels for each column, and at least 3 correct pairs of values

- 4 points for a graph of the values in the table (1) with a title(1), labels(1), and correct intervals(1) on both axes

- 3 points for part (b), one for the correct answer and two for the correct explanation or work shown

- 1 point for a correct rule written with symbols

### QUESTION 2: 6 POINTS

- One point for each of the following parts included in a story: as time increases (1), money should steadily increase (1) quickly (1) and then decrease (1) at a steady (1) but slower (1) rate

### QUESTION 3: 6 POINTS

- One point for each of the following parts of the description: In January there are 10 hours of daylight (1) and the amount of daylight increases until June (1), then decreases during the summer and falls (1) until it reaches 10 hours again in December (1). The amount of daylight increases the at the greatest rate from February to March (1) and decreases at the greatest rate from September to October (1)

### QUESTION 4: 15 POINTS

- Part (a) – 5 points for correct tables with titles, labels for each column, and at least 3 pairs of values

- Part (b) – 4 points, two for correct rules and two points for correct work shown or explanations; most students will write their rule in the form $y = b + mx$

- Part (c) – 3 points, one for the correct answer and two for the correct explanation or work shown

- Part (d) – 3 points, one for the correct answer and two for the correct explanation or work shown

### QUESTION 5: 9 POINTS

- 5 points given for a correct table with 10 entries and a label for each column

- 2 points for a correct equation using a correct coefficient for $x$ and the correct constant term, and 2 points for work shown or correct explanation.

## Grading Scale

| Points | Grade |
|--------|-------|
| 45 to 50 | A |
| 40 to 44 | B |
| 35 to 39 | C |
| 30 to 34 | D |

# Sample 1

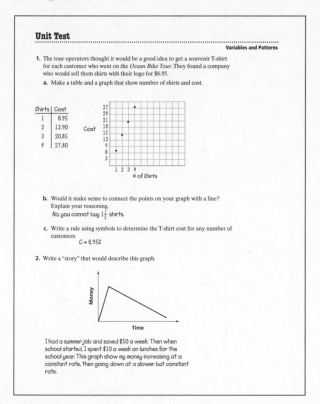

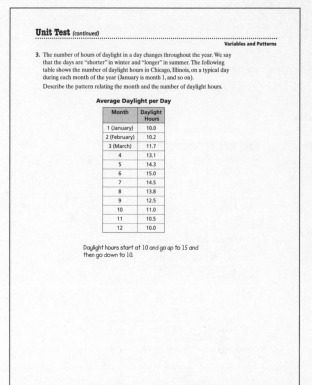

## A Teacher's Comments on Sample 1

Using the scoring rubric, Sample 1 receives a score of 34 points.

Question 1 received a total of 12 points. The student was able to make a correct table and graph, gave a correct explanation for not connecting the points on the graph, and was able to correctly write a rule that described the situation. However, the student did not title the table or the graph and lost 2 points.

Question 2 received all 6 of the possible points. The student was able to describe a situation where as time increased (weeks), money increased steadily and quickly ($50 a week), then as time continued to increase money decreased at a steady but slower rate ($10 a week).

For Question 3, the student received only 2 of the 6 possible points. The student was able to recognize that the number of hours of daylight increased and then decreased, but did not mention when the pattern changed, when the greatest increase or decrease occurred and that the number of hours of daylight in the last entry in December was the same amount that the table showed in the first entry in January.

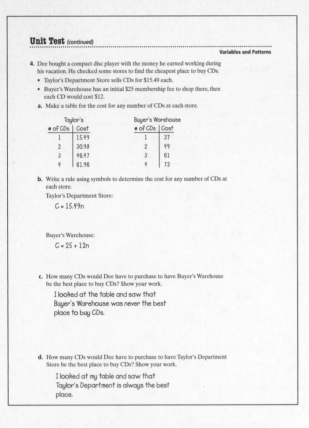

4. Dee bought a compact disc player with the money he earned working during his vacation. He checked some stores to find the cheapest place to buy CDs.
   • Taylor's Department Store sells CDs for $15.49 each.
   • Buyer's Warehouse has an initial $25 membership fee to shop there, then each CD would cost $12.
   a. Make a table for the cost for any number of CDs at each store.

Taylor's

| # of CDs | Cost |
|---|---|
| 1 | 15.49 |
| 2 | 30.98 |
| 3 | 46.47 |
| 4 | 61.96 |

Buyer's Warehouse

| # of CDs | Cost |
|---|---|
| 1 | 37 |
| 2 | 49 |
| 3 | 61 |
| 4 | 73 |

   b. Write a rule using symbols to determine the cost for any number of CDs at each store.
   Taylor's Department Store:
   $$C = 15.49n$$

   Buyer's Warehouse:
   $$C = 25 + 12n$$

   c. How many CDs would Dee have to purchase to have Buyer's Warehouse be the best place to buy CDs? Show your work.
   *I looked at the table and saw that Buyer's Warehouse was never the best place to buy CDs.*

   d. How many CDs would Dee have to purchase to have Taylor's Department Store be the best place to buy CDs? Show your work.
   *I looked at my table and saw that Taylor's Department is always the best place.*

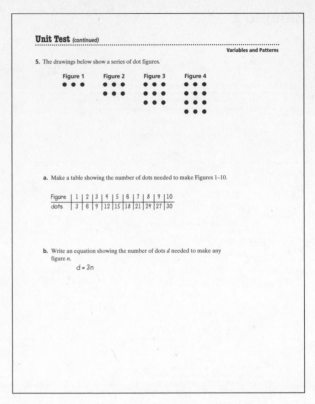

5. The drawings below show a series of dot figures.

Figure 1   Figure 2   Figure 3   Figure 4

   a. Make a table showing the number of dots needed to make Figures 1–10.

| Figure | 1 | 2 | 3 | 4 | 5 | 6 | 7 | 8 | 9 | 10 |
|---|---|---|---|---|---|---|---|---|---|---|
| dots | 3 | 6 | 9 | 12 | 15 | 18 | 21 | 24 | 27 | 30 |

   b. Write an equation showing the number of dots *d* needed to make any figure *n*.
   $$d = 3n$$

The student received a total of 7 points for question 4. The student was able to complete a table for each of the stores correctly for 5 points. The student was able to write rules for determining the cost for each store correctly for 2 points, but the student did not show work or explain their thinking describing how they arrived at the equations. It appears that the student only examined the tables up to 4 CDs when answering parts (c) and (d). The student did not use the rules or extend the tables and therefore answered both questions incorrectly.

The student received 7 points for question 5. The student was able to complete the table showing the number of dots needed to make Figures 1–10. The student correctly wrote an equation for describing the relationship in the table, but did not show work or explain their thinking.

The assessment work indicates that the task was appropriate and the student had an understanding tables and graphs. The student did at times fail to label both tables and graphs, but since the student did label some, it is likely that the student made careless errors. The student does seem to show an understanding of the relationships shown in a graph and is able to describe how as the values of x change the values of y will change. The student seems to have an understanding of how to continue a linear relationship and how to use variables to describe patterns. The part of the assessment that should most concern the teacher is the student's failure to look beyond the values in the table to compare two linear patterns with different patterns of change or to compare the patterns by solving equations. It appears that the student has some basic knowledge of linear relationships, but the depth of understanding of the meaning of the equations may be lacking.

# Sample 2

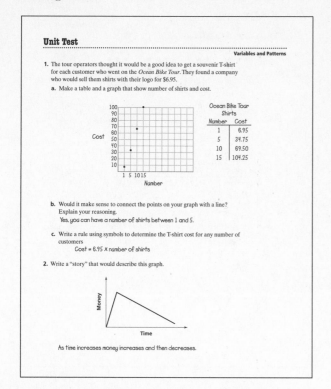

1. The tour operators thought it would be a good idea to get a souvenir T-shirt for each customer who went on the *Ocean Bike Tour*. They found a company who would sell them shirts with their logo for $6.95.

   a. Make a table and a graph that show number of shirts and cost.

   | Ocean Bike Tour Shirts | |
   |---|---|
   | Number | Cost |
   | 1 | 6.95 |
   | 5 | 34.75 |
   | 10 | 69.50 |
   | 15 | 104.25 |

   b. Would it make sense to connect the points on your graph with a line? Explain your reasoning.
   *Yes, you can have a number of shirts between 1 and 5.*

   c. Write a rule using symbols to determine the T-shirt cost for any number of customers
   *Cost = 6.95 × number of shirts*

2. Write a "story" that would describe this graph.

   *As time increases money increases and then decreases.*

3. The number of hours of daylight in a day changes throughout the year. We say that the days are "shorter" in winter and "longer" in summer. The following table shows the number of daylight hours in Chicago, Illinois, on a typical day during each month of the year (January is month 1, and so on).

   Describe the pattern relating the month and the number of daylight hours.

   **Average Daylight per Day**

   | Month | Daylight Hours |
   |---|---|
   | 1 (January) | 10.0 |
   | 2 (February) | 10.2 |
   | 3 (March) | 11.7 |
   | 4 | 13.1 |
   | 5 | 14.3 |
   | 6 | 15.0 |
   | 7 | 14.5 |
   | 8 | 13.8 |
   | 9 | 12.5 |
   | 10 | 11.0 |
   | 11 | 10.5 |
   | 12 | 10.0 |

   *Daylight hours start at 10 and go up to 15 and then go down to 10.*

## A Teacher's Comments on Sample 2

Using the scoring rubric, Sample 2 receives a score of 30 points.

Question 1 received a total of 9 points. The student earned 6 points for the table with correct title, labels, and values. The student only received 2 points for the graph since the title was missing and the interval on the x-axis was not consistent. For part (b), the student only received 1 point. Although the student did not state that it does not make sense to buy a portion of a shirt, the student correctly reasoned that there are numbers of shirts that can be bought between the values graphed. The student would not receive any points for part (c) since the rule was not written using symbols and there was no explanation.

Question 2 is worth 1 point since the student did not write a "story" as directed, and only mentioned money increasing and then decreasing. There was no comparison in the rate of the increase with the rate of the decrease, and the student failed to mention that the increase or decrease was a steady one.

The student received only 1 of the possible 6 points for question 3. The student did describe the daylight hours as increasing to 15 and then decreasing to 10. However, the student did not describe how the increase or decrease was not constant, or describe when the increase or decrease showed the greatest change. No mention was made about the months that showed the same daylight hours.

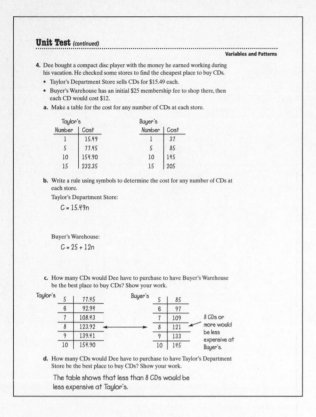

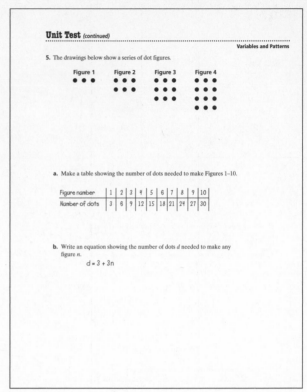

Question 4 received a total of 13 points. The student was able to correctly and completely show tables that represented the price for both stores. The student also correctly identified rules that described this relationship but did not explain any thinking or show any work. In parts (c) and (d) the student noticed the values in the table where the rates changed. The student investigated values between those in the table and found the specific amounts for the best deals. Although the student did not use the equations to determine when one store had a better deal, the student used a valid method by examining the tables in detail.

The student received 6 points for question 5. The student completed the table and wrote an equation for the relationship using the correct slope. However, the student included an incorrect constant term (starting point) with no work shown.

The assessment work indicates that the task was appropriate and that the student had a general understanding of linear relationships. Some of the work showed great attention to detail as in the use of the tables in question 4. The student appears to understand that the relationship shown in the tables involve more than the given points. The student was able to take a part of the table and investigate it more closely to see where the different patterns of change made an impact on the price. The student may not have that same understanding of the relationship when thinking about the rules and the coefficient of $x$. Since the student did not use the rules, it is difficult to determine how much is understood.

The student was able to write correct rules in questions 1 and 4, but made a mistake in the rule for question 5. It appears that the student has some understanding of writing rules to describe relationships but appeared to be careless in question 5. Carelessness may also be the reason that the student did not use symbols when writing the rule for question 1, since the student was proficient in question 4.

The descriptions that the student in sample 2 used to write the story and to describe the pattern for the tables in question 3 were lacking detail. The descriptions were too broad and general. This is certainly an area that, with thought and attention to details, can demonstrate a greater understanding in the relationships.

Although this student has an understanding of linear relationships and the ways to model them, this student may need time to develop sound mathematical habits.

# Check-Up 1

1. Stefan said he had done an experiment similar to the jumping jack exercise. He had collected data on the number of deep knee bends a person could do in 2 minutes. The graph below shows his data.

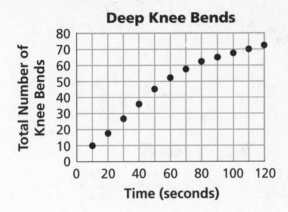

**Deep Knee Bends**

   a. What are the two variables?

   b. Make a table of Stefan's data.

   c. Describe in detail how the number of deep knee bends changes as time increases.

   d. From Stefan's data estimate the number knee bends he had done in 25 seconds and in 65 seconds. Explain how you made those estimates.

## Check-Up 1 (continued)

2. The table shows some data Anita collected while walking.

**Anita's Walk**

| Time (minutes) | 0 | 5 | 10 | 15 | 20 | 25 | 30 |
|---|---|---|---|---|---|---|---|
| Distance (miles) | 0 | 0.5 | 1 | 1.25 | 1.5 | 1.75 | 1.8 |

   **a.** What are the two variables?

   **b.** Graph the data from the table on the axes below.

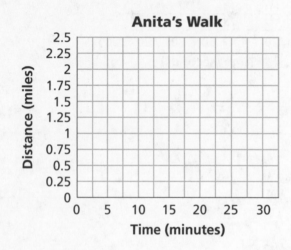

   **c.** In what time periods did Anita make the most progress?

      How does this show up in the table?

      How does this show up in the graph?

   **d.** In what time periods did Anita make the least progress?

      How does this show up in the table?

      How does this show up in the graph?

# Check-Up 2

**1.** Teresa baby-sits for $4.50 an hour.

 **a.** Make a table showing how much money she will make over time.

 **b.** Graph your data, label the axes and name the graph.

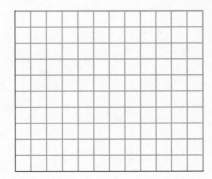

 **c.** Does it make sense to connect the points on the graph? Why or why not?

 **d.** About how many hours does Teresa have to baby-sit to earn $20? Explain your answer.

 **e.** If Teresa baby-sits 5.5 hours, how much will she earn? Explain your answer.

# Check-Up 2 (continued)

**2.** The three graphs below show the progress of a cyclist at different times during a ride. For each graph, describe the rider's progress over the time interval.

**a.**

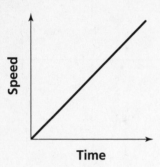

**b.**

**c.**

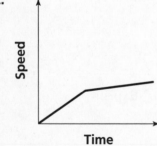

## Check-Up 2 (continued)

3. The graph below shows the number of cans of food collected by Mr. Darrow's students on each of the five days of the school's food drive.

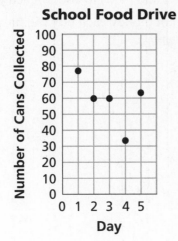

**School Food Drive**

a. The graph shows the relationship between two variables. What are the variables?

b. On which day were the most cans of food collected?

How many cans were collected on that day?

c. What was the total number of cans collected over the 5 days? Explain your reasoning.

d. Does it make sense to connect the points with line segments? Explain your reasoning.

# Partner Quiz

**1.** Dominic and Norm decide to save their money to go on a bike tour in their state. Dominic thinks he can save $10 per week.

Norm has $25 from his birthday to start with and plans to add $7 each week.

**a.** Make a table that will show the amount of money each boy will have over the next ten weeks if they stick to their plans.

**b.** Write a rule to show how much money each boy has for any number of weeks.

Dominic:

Norm:

## Partner Quiz (continued)

**c.** Use the entries in your tables to graph each boy's savings over time. Label the axes and name your graph. Use a different color to graph the data for each boy.

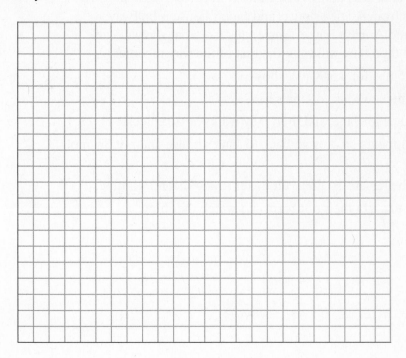

**d.** Will the boys ever have the same amount of money at the same time? Explain your reasoning.

**e.** If the bike tour costs $190, when will each boy have enough money to go on the tour?

**Partner Quiz** *(continued)*

**2.** Read the following story carefully. Then, make a table and a graph for the story. Be sure to label your axes and the table rows and name your graph and table.

Angie and her friend Jane are going to see a movie at the Civic Theater. The theater is eight blocks from Angie's house, and Jane's house is halfway between the theater and Angie's house. Angie tells Jane that she will walk over to her house and then they will walk the rest of the way together.

- Angie leaves at 4:25 P.M. for a 5:00 P.M. show.
- It takes her 10 minutes to walk to Jane's house.
- She waits five minutes for Jane, and then they walk for two blocks.
- Jane's dog Gizmo appears, so they go back to Jane's house and put Gizmo inside.
- They are afraid of being late, so they run to get to the theater on time.
- They arrive at 4:56 P.M., get their popcorn, and watch the show.

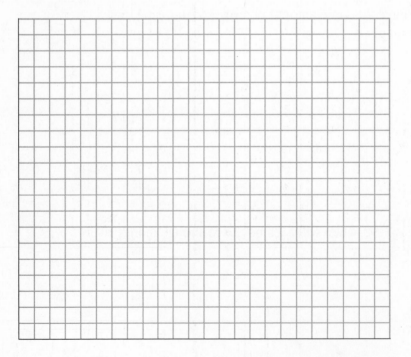

Name _____ Date _____ Class _____

# Multiple-Choice Items

**1.** What is the value of *y* when *x* is 68?

| x | y |
|---|---|
| 92 | 23 |
| 96 | 24 |
| 100 | 25 |
| 104 | 26 |
| 108 | 27 |

**A.** 17          **B.** 18          **C.** 16          **D.** 19

**2.** Data was collected on a student's typing rate. A line that best fits the data points was drawn on the graph. Approximately how many words had this student typed in 30 seconds?

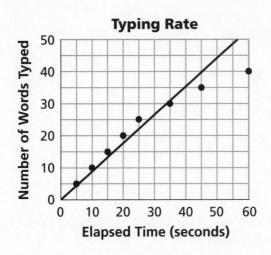

**F.** 20          **G.** 24          **H.** 28          **J.** 34

**3.** If *y* = 12 + 3.5*x*, what is the value of *y* when *x* = 10?

**A.** 25.5          **B.** 155          **C.** 47          **D.** 362

## Multiple-Choice Items (continued)

**4.** The equation $c = 0.75t$ represents the total cost of tickets for carnival games. Which table best represents this equation?

**F.**

| Tickets | 1 | 2 | 3 | 4 |
|---------|------|------|------|------|
| Cost | $0.75 | $1.50 | $2.25 | $3.00 |

**G.**

| Tickets | 1 | 2 | 3 | 4 |
|---------|------|------|------|------|
| Cost | $0.75 | $1.00 | $1.25 | $1.50 |

**H.**

| Tickets | 1 | 2 | 3 | 4 |
|---------|------|------|------|------|
| Cost | $1.75 | $2.50 | $3.25 | $4.00 |

**J.**

| Tickets | 1 | 2 | 3 | 4 |
|---------|------|------|------|------|
| Cost | $0.75 | $1.75 | $2.50 | $4.75 |

**5.** Which problem situation matches the equation below?

$$6x = 90$$

**A.** Hahn exercised 90 minutes each day for 6 days this month. What is the total number of hours $x$ that he exercised this month?

**B.** Tori charges $6 per hour to cut lawns. What is the number of hours $x$ that Tori worked if she charged $90 for her labor?

**C.** Lizzie drove a total of 90 miles this week. She drove 6 miles more than last week. What is the number of miles $x$ that Lizzie drove last week?

**D.** Gustav had saved $90. He gave 6% to his six-year-old sister. What is the amount $x$ that he has left?

## Multiple-Choice Items (continued)

**6.** If $y = x - 19$, what is the value of $x$ when $y = 34$?

    **F.** 15            **G.** 53            **H.** −15            **J.** −53

**7.** Which equation shows the relationship between $x$ and $y$ shown in the graph?

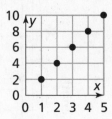

    **A.** $y = x + 2$     **B.** $y = 2x$     **C.** $y = 2x + 2$     **D.** $y = x$

**8.** Which of the following best explains how the following pattern is formed?

    2  3  5  8  13 ...

    **F.** Multiply each number by the number before it

    **G.** Add 1, add 2, add 3 and so on

    **H.** Multiply by 2 and subtract 1

    **J.** Add the previous two numbers together to get the new number

# Multiple-Choice Items (continued)

**9.** Which graph best represents the table below?

| Length of Side of a Square | 1 | 2 | 3 | 4 | 5 |
|---|---|---|---|---|---|
| Perimeter | 4 | 8 | 12 | 16 | 20 |

**A.**
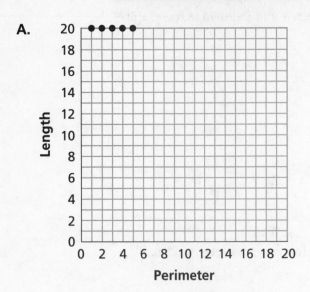

**B.**
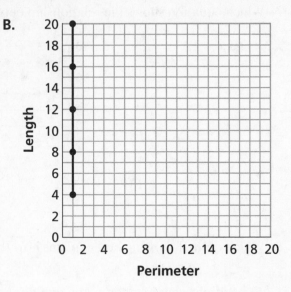

**C.**
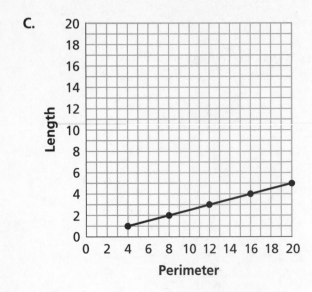

**D.**
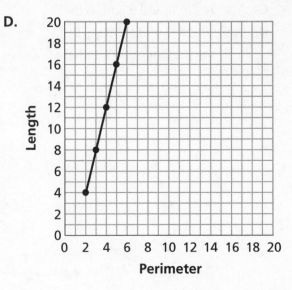

Name _____ Date _____ Class _____

# Notebook Checklist

**Place a ✓ next to each item you have completed.**

## Notebook Organization

_____ Problems and Mathematical Reflections are labeled and dated.

_____ Work is neat and easy to find and follow.

## Vocabulary

_____ All words are listed.     _____ All words are defined or described.

## Assessments

_____ Check-Up 1          _____ Partner Quiz

_____ Check-Up 2          _____ Unit Test

## Assignments

_____  _____     _____  _____

_____  _____     _____  _____

_____  _____     _____  _____

_____  _____     _____  _____

_____  _____     _____  _____

_____  _____     _____  _____

_____  _____     _____  _____

_____  _____     _____  _____

_____  _____     _____  _____

_____  _____     _____  _____

_____  _____     _____  _____

_____  _____     _____  _____

_____  _____     _____  _____

_____  _____     _____  _____

_____  _____     _____  _____

_____  _____     _____  _____

_____  _____     _____  _____

# Self Assessment

## Mathematical Ideas

Situations that change are a part of everyone's life. Some situations change in a predictable pattern. Other situations change in ways that seem beyond our ability to anticipate. After studying the mathematics in *Variables and Patterns*:

**1. a.** I learned these things about variables, patterns, and how tables, graphs, and rules can help me find and describe patterns:

**b.** Here are page numbers of notebook entries that give evidence of what I have learned, along with descriptions of what each entry shows:

**2. a.** The mathematical ideas that I am still struggling with:

**b.** This is why I think these ideas are difficult for me:

**c.** Here are page numbers of notebook entries that give evidence of what I am struggling with, along with descriptions of what each entry shows:

## Class Participation

I contributed to the classroom **discussion** and understanding of *Variables and Patterns* when I . . . (Give examples.)

# Self Assessment (continued)

## Learning Environment

**Rate the learning activities using this scale:**

**1** I consistently struggled to understand the mathematics and I'm still not sure that I know it.

**2** I struggled somewhat but now I understand more than I did.

**3** I had to work, but I feel confident that I understand now.

**4** I understood everything pretty easily and I feel confident that I know the mathematics in these problems.

**5** Everything came easily. I knew most of the mathematics before we did this.

### Learning Activities:

_____ Problems from the Investigations

_____ ACE Homework Assignments

_____ Mathematical Reflections

_____ Check-Ups

_____ Partner Quiz

_____ Unit Test

**Check any of the following that you feel are the most helpful in adding to the success of your learning.**

❏ Working on my own in class.

❏ Discussing a problem with a partner.

❏ Working in a small group of 3 or 4 people.

❏ Discussing a problem as a whole class.

❏ Individual or group presentation to the whole class.

❏ Hearing how other people solved the problem.

❏ Summarizing the mathematics as a class and taking notes.

❏ Completing homework assignments.

# Unit Test

1. The tour operators thought it would be a good idea to get a souvenir T-shirt for each customer who went on the *Ocean Bike Tour*. They found a company who would sell them shirts with their logo for $6.95.

   **a.** Make a table and a graph that show number of shirts and cost.

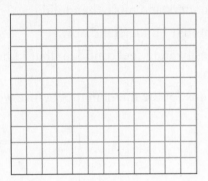

   **b.** Would it make sense to connect the points on your graph with a line? Explain your reasoning.

   **c.** Write a rule using symbols to determine the T-shirt cost for any number of customers

2. Write a "story" that would describe this graph.

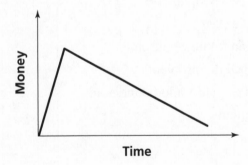

Name _____ Date _____ Class _____

# Unit Test *(continued)*

**Variables and Patterns**

**3.** The number of hours of daylight in a day changes throughout the year. We say that the days are "shorter" in winter and "longer" in summer. The following table shows the number of daylight hours in Chicago, Illinois, on a typical day during each month of the year (January is month 1, and so on).

Describe the pattern relating the month and the number of daylight hours.

**Average Daylight per Day**

| Month | Daylight Hours |
|---|---|
| 1 (January) | 10.0 |
| 2 (February) | 10.2 |
| 3 (March) | 11.7 |
| 4 | 13.1 |
| 5 | 14.3 |
| 6 | 15.0 |
| 7 | 14.5 |
| 8 | 13.8 |
| 9 | 12.5 |
| 10 | 11.0 |
| 11 | 10.5 |
| 12 | 10.0 |

© Pearson Education, Inc., publishing as Pearson Prentice Hall. All rights reserved.

**17**

## Unit Test *(continued)*

**4.** Dee bought a compact disc player with the money he earned working during his vacation. He checked some stores to find the cheapest place to buy CDs.

- Taylor's Department Store sells CDs for $15.49 each.
- Buyer's Warehouse has an initial $25 membership fee to shop there, then each CD would cost $12.

**a.** Make a table for the cost for any number of CDs at each store.

**b.** Write a rule using symbols to determine the cost for any number of CDs at each store.

Taylor's Department Store:

Buyer's Warehouse:

**c.** How many CDs would Dee have to purchase to have Buyer's Warehouse be the best place to buy CDs? Show your work.

**d.** How many CDs would Dee have to purchase to have Taylor's Department Store be the best place to buy CDs? Show your work.

# Unit Test (continued)

**5.** The drawings below show a series of dot figures.

| Figure 1 | Figure 2 | Figure 3 | Figure 4 |

    **a.** Make a table showing the number of dots needed to make Figures 1–10.

    **b.** Write an equation showing the number of dots $d$ needed to make any figure $n$.

# Question Bank

Assign these questions as additional homework, or use them as review, quiz, or test questions.

**1.** The table shows some data Carmen collected during her swim team practice.

**Carmen's Swim**

| Number of Breaths | 0 | 1 | 2 | 3 | 4 | 5 | 6 | 7 |
|---|---|---|---|---|---|---|---|---|
| Number of Meters Swum | 0 | 5 | 8 | 12 | 15 | 17 | 20 | 24 |

**a.** What are the two variables?

**b.** Graph the data from the table on the axes below.

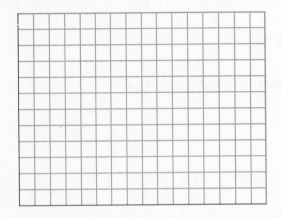

**c.** Does it make sense to connect the points? Explain your reasoning.

**d.** When did Carmen make the most progress?

   **i.** How does this show up in the table?

   **ii.** How does this show up in the graph?

**e.** When did Carmen make the least progress?

   **i.** How does this show up in the table?

   **ii.** How does this show up in the graph?

**f.** How many breaths do you think she would take if she swam 50 meters?

**2.** The graph below shows data that Elizabeth collected while walking.

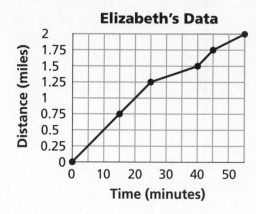

**Elizabeth's Data**

**a.** When does she make the most progress? Explain your reasoning.

**b.** When does she make the least progress? Explain your reasoning.

**3.** The following sketch shows the diagonals that can be drawn from one vertex of a pentagon. The diagonals split the pentagon into three triangular regions. The same sort of triangulation can be done in other polygons as well.

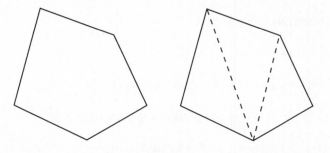

**a.** Draw polygons of 4, 5, 6, 7, 8, 9, and 10 sides. In each, pick one vertex and draw all possible diagonals from that vertex. Make a table to record the number of diagonals drawn in the different polygons. Leave room in your table to add another row of information from part (c).

**b.** Find a pattern that predicts the number of diagonals that can be drawn from one vertex in a polygon. Write the pattern as a rule using $n$ for the number of sides and $d$ for the number of diagonals. Verify your formula using any three of the figures you sketched for part (a).

**c.** Count the number of regions that the diagonals form in the polygons. Record your results in the table you made for part (a).

**d.** Find a pattern relating number of sides in a polygon to the number of regions formed by drawing diagonals from one vertex. Write your pattern in symbolic form, using $n$ for number of sides and $r$ for number of regions formed.

**e.** Use the rule you wrote in part (d) to calculate the number of regions formed in each of the following polygons.

  **i.** 20 sides      **ii.** 50 sides      **iii.** 1000 sides      **iv.** 1,000,000 sides

**4.** Each day the cafeteria workers at Edison Middle School start out with 400 cartons of milk. They collected some data and made the following graph.

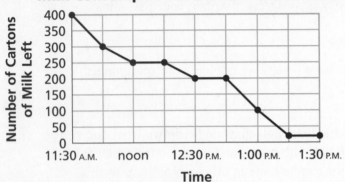

**Milk Consumption at Edison Middle School**

**a.** What is the total number of cartons of milk sold?

**b.** How many cartons were sold between noon and 12:30 P.M.?

**c.** During what 15-minute time period(s) was the most milk sold?

**d.** During what 15-minute time period(s) was the least amount of milk sold?

**e.** Describe how the total number of cartons of milk available changed as the day progressed.

**f.** Should the cafeteria workers have connected the points? Explain.

**g.** Would a table be useful? Explain.

**5.** Hiroshi gave $y = 8x$ as the answer to a question on his test paper. Make up a situation that his rule could represent.

**6.** Mary and Juanita made the following graphs.

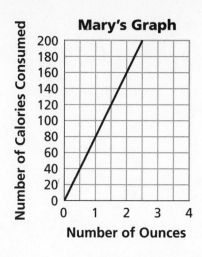

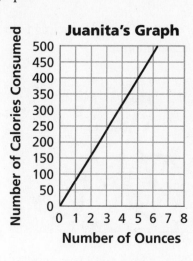

**a.** Did Mary and Juanita graph the same data set? Explain your reasoning.

**b.** Write a rule relating the number of ounces to the calories consumed from Mary's graph.

**7.** Francisco was working on a problem on his graphing calculator. He saw the following two screens.

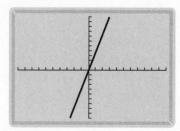

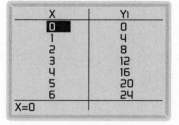

His partner made a sketch of the two screens. Then, he accidentally cleared the rule from the screen.

**a.** Write a rule that would make this graph and table.

**b.** Give a situation that could be represented by your rule.

# Check-Up 1

1. The coach took a digital photo of the new cycling team bike. She sent an 8 cm by 10 cm photo to each team member.

   **a.** If the photo were enlarged by a scale factor of 150% of its original size, what would be the new length and width?

   **b.** Imagine you want to make a 2 cm by 2.5 cm copy of the original photo. What percent should you use?

   **c.** What scale factor relates the side lengths in the original photo to those in the smaller photo?

   **d.** How will the angles in the original photo compare to the corresponding angles in the smaller photo?

   **e.** How will the perimeter of the original photo compare to that of the smaller photo?

   **f.** Find the areas of the original and the smaller photos. How do these areas compare?

# Check-Up 2

1. While designing a video game, Victor drew parallelogram *ABCD* with vertex coordinates (1,1), (4,4), (8,4) and (5,1) like the one on the coordinate grid below.

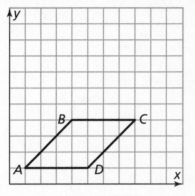

  a. Find the area and perimeter of parallelogram *ABCD*.

   Area =                              Perimeter =

  b. Draw another rectangle *EFGH* with vertex coordinates related to parallelogram *ABCD* by the rule $(0.5x, 0.5y)$.

| Point | (x, y) |
|-------|--------|
| A | (1, 1) |
| B | (4, 4) |
| C | (8, 4) |
| D | (5, 1) |

| Point | (0.5x, 0.5y) |
|-------|--------------|
| E | |
| F | |
| G | |
| H | |

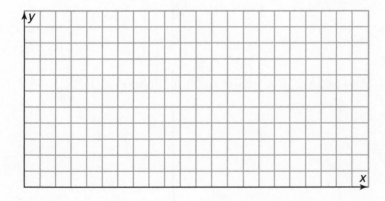

  c. Find the area and perimeter of parallelogram *EFGH*.

   Area =                              Perimeter =

Name _____ Date _____ Class _____

**d.** Draw another parallelogram *JKLM* with vertex coordinates related to parallelogram *ABCD* by the rule (2*x*, 1.5*y*).

| Point | (x, y) |
|-------|--------|
| A | (1, 1) |
| B | (4, 4) |
| C | (8, 4) |
| D | (5, 1) |

| Point | (2x, 1.5y) |
|-------|------------|
| J | |
| K | |
| L | |
| M | |

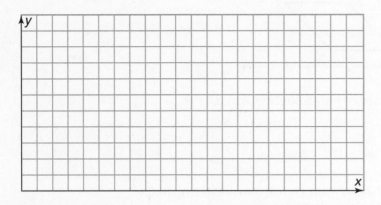

**e.** Find the area and perimeter of parallelogram *JKLM*.

Area =                          Perimeter =

**f.** Which parallelogram, *EFGH* or *JKLM*, is similar to parallelogram *ABCD*? Justify your answer.

## Check-Up 2

**2.** Which rectangles below are similar? How do you know?

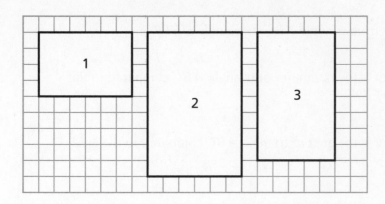

**3.** These triangles are similar.

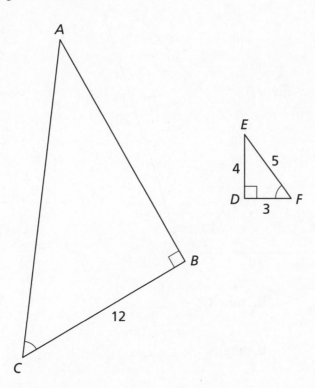

**a.** What are the lengths of sides *AC* and *AB*?

side *AC* = _____ side *AB* = _____

# Check-Up 2

**b.** What is the scale factor from triangle *DEF* to triangle *ABC*?

**c.** What is the scale factor from triangle *ABC* to triangle *DEF*?

**d.** How many times greater is the perimeter of triangle *ABC* compared to the perimeter of triangle *DEF*?

**e.** How many times greater is the area of triangle *ABC* compared to the area of triangle *DEF*?

**4.** The two triangles are similar. Find the missing measurements.

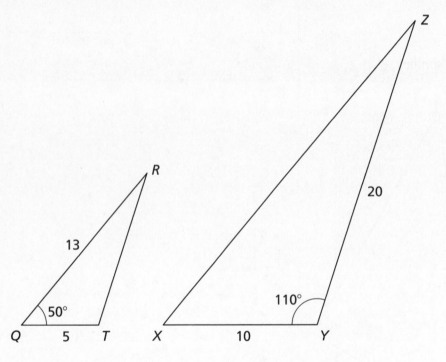

**a.** side *TR* = _____       **b.** side *XZ* = _____

**c.** angle *T* = _____       **d.** angle *Z* = _____

# Partner Quiz

1. Ryan drew a one-eyed triangle character on dot paper. Ashley used the rule $(3x, 3y)$ to enlarge Ryan's drawing and she drew the character below.

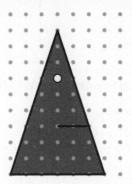

   **a.** Simone saw Ashley's drawing and doubled all the lengths to create her own character. On the grids below, sketch Ryan's original character and Simone's new version of Ashley's character.

   **Ryan's One-eyed Character**          **Simone's One-eyed Character**

   **b.** Are Ryan's and Simone's characters similar? Explain.

   **c.** Write a rule that would create Simone's character from Ryan's character.

# Partner Quiz *(continued)*

2. Megan wanted to make a new video game character.

   **a.** Write a rule that would transform Mug $(x, y)$ (see Problem/Labsheet 2.1) into Slug who is very wide and not very tall.

   **b.** Megan wanted Slug to move up (but not over) on the grid. What rule could do this for her?

   **c.** Is Slug similar to Mug? Why or why not?

3. Are shapes A and B similar? Explain your answer.

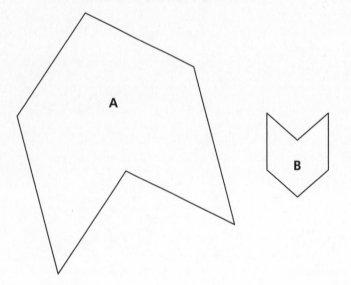

# Multiple-Choice Items

1. Nora has two picture frames that have identical shapes but different sizes. The larger frame is 3 ft wide by 6 ft high. What is the measurement of the height of the other frame if it is 2 ft wide?

   **A.** 3 ft        **B.** 4 ft        **C.** 9 ft        **D.** 1 ft

2. Tatenda has a chocolate chip cookie recipe that uses $2\frac{1}{2}$ cups of sugar for 6 dozen cookies. How much sugar will he need if he only wants to make 36 cookies?

   **F.** $1\frac{1}{4}$ cup        **G.** 5 cups        **H.** 2 cups        **J.** $1\frac{1}{2}$ cups

3. A scale of a map indicates that "1 inch equals 75 miles." How many miles does 6 inches represent?

   **A.** 81 miles        **B.** 375 miles        **C.** 450 miles        **D.** 525 miles

4. Natasha wants to enlarge one of her favorite pictures. She takes her pictures to a store that has a photo enlarger. The dimensions of her original picture are 4 inches by 6 inches. If the she enters 150% into the enlarger, what will be the new dimensions of Natasha's picture?

   **F.** $6'' \times 9''$        **G.** $2'' \times 3''$        **H.** $8'' \times 12''$        **J.** $200'' \times 300''$

# Notebook Checklist

**Place a ✓ next to each item you have completed.**

## Notebook Organization

_____ Problems and Mathematical Reflections are labeled and dated.

_____ Work is neat and easy to find and follow.

## Vocabulary

_____ All words are listed.      _____ All words are defined or described.

## Assessments

_____ Check-Up 1          _____ Partner Quiz

_____ Check-Up 2          _____ Unit Test

## Assignments

_____ _____      _____ _____

_____ _____      _____ _____

_____ _____      _____ _____

_____ _____      _____ _____

_____ _____      _____ _____

_____ _____      _____ _____

_____ _____      _____ _____

_____ _____      _____ _____

_____ _____      _____ _____

_____ _____      _____ _____

_____ _____      _____ _____

_____ _____      _____ _____

_____ _____      _____ _____

_____ _____      _____ _____

_____ _____      _____ _____

_____ _____      _____ _____

_____ _____      _____ _____

# Self Assessment

**Mathematical Ideas**

We hear the word similar often. People use it to talk about things that are alike in some way. In *Stretching and Shrinking,* I learned what the word similar means in the mathematical sense and how I can use the idea of similarity to solve some interesting problems.

1. **a.** I learned these things about mathematical similarity and what happens to lengths, areas, and angles when you stretch and enlarge figures:

   **b.** Here are page numbers of notebook entries that give evidence of what I have learned, along with descriptions of what each entry shows:

2. **a.** The mathematical ideas that I am still struggling with:

   **b.** This is why I think these ideas are difficult for me:

   **c.** Here are page numbers of notebook entries that give evidence of what I am struggling with, along with descriptions of what each entry shows:

**Class Participation**

I contributed to the classroom **discussion** and understanding of *Stretching and Shrinking* when I . . . (Give examples.)

# Self Assessment (continued)

**Learning Environment**

**Rate the learning activities using this scale:**

**1**    I consistently struggled to understand the mathematics and I'm still not sure that I know it.

**2**    I struggled somewhat but now I understand more than I did.

**3**    I had to work, but I feel confident that I understand now.

**4**    I understood everything pretty easily and I feel confident that I know the mathematics in these problems.

**5**    Everything came easily. I knew most of the mathematics before we did this.

**Learning Activities:**

_____ Problems from the Investigations

_____ ACE Homework Assignments

_____ Mathematical Reflections

_____ Check-Ups

_____ Partner Quiz

_____ Unit Test

**Check any of the following that you feel are the most helpful in adding to the success of your learning.**

❏    Working on my own in class.

❏    Discussing a problem with a partner.

❏    Working in a small group of 3 or 4 people.

❏    Discussing a problem as a whole class.

❏    Individual or group presentation to the whole class.

❏    Hearing how other people solved the problem.

❏    Summarizing the mathematics as a class and taking notes.

❏    Completing homework assignments.

# Unit Test

Use the following diagrams of the floor plans for a tree house before and after reduction and enlargement by a copier to answer Exercises 1–8.

**Original Tree House Floor Plan**

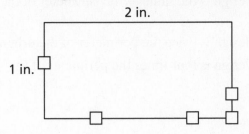

**Enlarged Tree House Floor Plan**

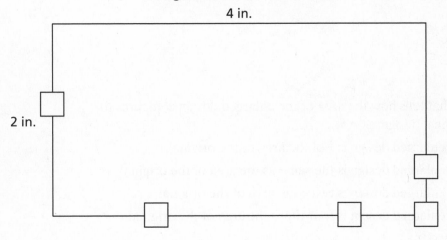

**Reduced Tree House Floor Plan**

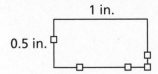

**1.** What is the scale factor from the original design to the enlarged design?

**2.** Circle the answer that tells how the perimeter of the enlarged design compares to the perimeter of the original design.

   **F.** The perimeter of the enlarged design is $\frac{1}{2}$ of the perimeter of the original.

   **G.** The perimeter of the enlarged design is the same as the perimeter of the original.

   **H.** The perimeter of the enlarged design is twice the perimeter of the original.

   **J.** The perimeter of the enlarged design is four times the perimeter of the original.

   Explain your answer.

**3.** Circle the answer that tells how the area of the enlarged design compares to the area of the original design.

   **A.** The area of the enlarged design is $\frac{1}{2}$ of the area of the original.

   **B.** The area of the enlarged design is the same as the area of the original.

   **C.** The area of the enlarged design is twice the area of the original.

   **D.** The area of the enlarged design is four times the area of the original.

   Explain your answer.

**4.** What copier size factor was used to make the enlarged design from the original?

**5.** What is the scale factor from the original design to the reduced design?

# Unit Test (continued)

**6.** Circle the answer that tells how the perimeter of the reduced design compares to the perimeter of the original design.

  **F.** The perimeter of the reduced design is $\frac{1}{2}$ of the perimeter of the original.

  **G.** The perimeter of the reduced design is the same as the perimeter of the original.

  **H.** The perimeter of the reduced design is $\frac{1}{4}$ of the perimeter of the original.

  **J.** The perimeter of the reduced design is four times the perimeter of the original.

  Explain your answer.

**7.** Circle the answer that tells how the area of the enlarged design compares to the area of the original design.

  **A.** The area of the reduced design is $\frac{1}{2}$ of the area of the original.

  **B.** The area of the reduced design is the same as the area of the original.

  **C.** The area of the reduced design is $\frac{1}{4}$ of the area of the original.

  **D.** The area of the reduced design is four times the area of the original.

  Explain your answer.

**8.** What copier size factor was used to make the reduced design from the original?

# Unit Test (continued)

9. The following table gives key coordinates for drawing a backpack for the Wumps. Backpack 1 is plotted on the grid.

   a. Find coordinates for drawing the other backpacks.

### Wump Backpacks

| Backpack 1 | Backpack 2 | Backpack 3 | Backpack 4 |
|------------|------------|------------|------------|
| $(x, y)$ | $(2x, 2y)$ | $(x + 8, y - 2)$ | $(x, 2y)$ |
| (0, 2) | | | |
| (8, 2) | | | |
| (6, 5) | | | |
| (2, 5) | | | |
| (0, 2) | | | |

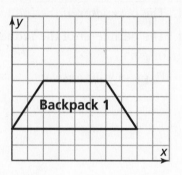

   b. Plot Backpack 2, Backpack 3, and Backpack 4 on the following grids.

### Grid for Backpack 2

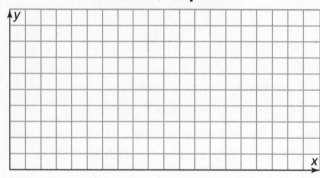

### Grid for Backpack 3

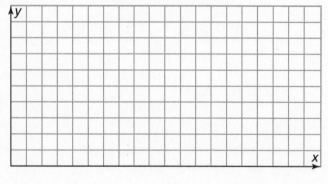

**Unit Test** (continued)

**Grid for Backpack 4**

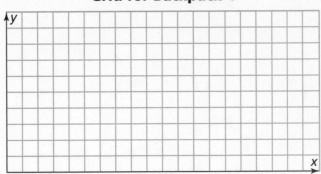

c. Which backpacks are similar? Explain.

10. Use these two similar parallelograms to answer the questions below.

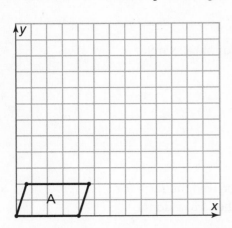 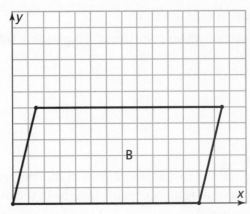

a. Write a rule that finds coordinates of any point on Parallelogram A from the corresponding point on Parallelogram B.

b. Write a rule that finds coordinates of any point on Parallelogram B from the corresponding point on Parallelogram A.

c. What is the scale factor that relates Parallelogram A to Parallelogram B?

## Unit Test (continued)

**11.** Consider the two polygons below.

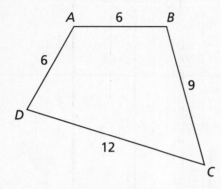 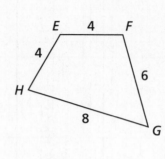

**a.** Does the diagram provide enough information to determine whether the two polygons are similar? If not, what additional information may you need?

**b.** Suppose the polygons are similar.

**i.** Write two ratios that compare corresponding sides of the similar polygons.

**ii.** Find the ratio of two adjacent sides in one polygon and the ratio for the corresponding adjacent side lengths in the other. How do the ratios compare?

**iii.** What scale factor relates the corresponding sides in the polygons above? Explain your answer.

# Unit Test *(continued)*

**12.** The following picture is in an 8 centimeter by 6 centimeter frame.

   **a.** Can this frame be reduced to 6 centimeters by 4 centimeters without distorting the shape? Explain.

   **b.** Can this frame be reduced to 4 centimeters by 3 centimeters without distorting the shape? Explain.

**13.** Consider the diagram below. $BC$ is parallel to $DE$.

   **a.** Name two similar triangles and state how you know they are similar.

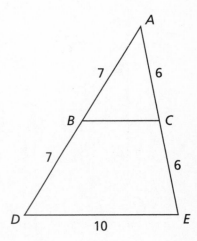

   **b.** What is the length of side $AE$?

   **c.** What is the length of line segment $BC$?

Name _____ Date _____ Class _____

# Unit Test (continued)

**14.** Use the diagram below to determine the height of the flagpole.

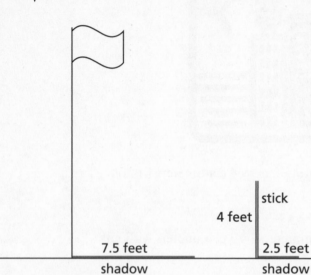

stick

4 feet

7.5 feet

2.5 feet

shadow

shadow

# Question Bank

1. The ratio of two adjacent side lengths of a rectangle is $\frac{2}{3}$. Which of these could be the ratio of two adjacent side lengths of a similar rectangle?

$$\frac{4}{9} \qquad \frac{4}{3} \qquad \frac{2}{6} \qquad \frac{4}{5} \qquad \frac{6}{9}$$

2. Which of the following rectangles is similar to a 10 by 15 rectangle?

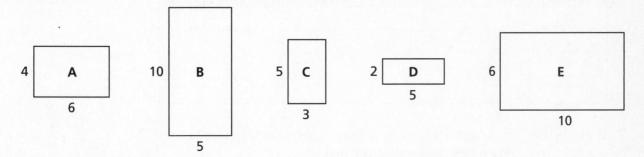

3. The Polygon Tool and Die Company has created a new logo (a symbol for their company). They want to stamp their logo on small, medium, and large pieces of equipment. The size of the logo must match the size of the equipment, but the logos must all be similar. Design a logo for Polygon Tool and Die, and sketch three similar figures for the logo. Explain how you know they are similar.

4. For parts (a)–(c), explain what would happen to a figure if you transformed it using the given rule.

   a. $(3x, 6y)$

   b. $(x + 2, y + 1)$

   c. $(2x, 2y + 5)$

5. The three rectangles below are similar. Find the missing measurements.

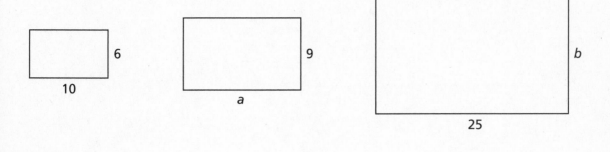

   $a =$                              $b =$

**6.** Rectangle A is sketched below. Complete the table for rectangles B, C, and D which are similar to rectangle A.

| Rectangle | Scale Factor | Short Side | Long Side | Perimeter | Area |
|-----------|--------------|------------|-----------|-----------|------|
| A | 1 | 1 | 4 | | |
| B | 3 | | | | |
| C | 10 | | | | |
| D | $\frac{1}{2}$ | | | | |

**7.** If two figures are similar, which of the following *might* be different? Circle your answers, and explain each choice you make.

number of sides                          size of angles

lengths of corresponding sides          ratio of corresponding sides

shape                                    area

**8.** A rectangle has dimensions of 1 and 6. Another rectangle was drawn from it using a scale factor of 1.5.

   **a.** The area of the large rectangle is how many times the area of the small rectangle?

   **b.** The perimeter of the large rectangle is how many times the perimeter of the small rectangle?

**9.** Gerald wanted to find the height of the flagpole at the entrance to his school. He used a mirror and recorded some measurements on a drawing. What is the height of the flagpole?

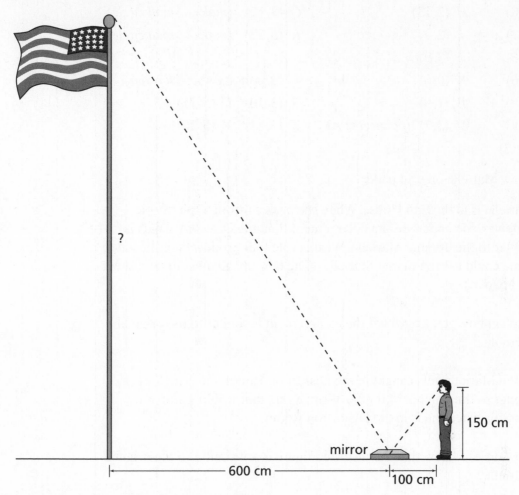

**10.** Below is a triangle and its image.

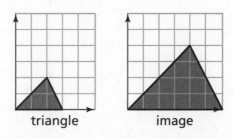

triangle              image

**a.** Which of these rules was used to make the image?

$(2x, 2y)$      $(x, 2y)$      $(2x, y)$      $(2x, 4y)$      $(4x, 2y)$

**b.** Are the triangle and its image similar? Explain.

**11.** Mariella is a character in the Amusement Park video game. She is made according to these coordinates:

| **Body** | | **Eyes** |
|---|---|---|
| *A* (4, 0) | *H* (2, 13) | *Q* (3, 12) *(make a small circle)* |
| *B* (5, 7) | *I* (2, 9) | *R* (5, 12) *(make a small circle)* |
| *C* (7, 5) | *J* (3, 9) | |
| *D* (8, 6) | *K* (0, 6) | **Mouth** *(connect in order)* |
| *E* (5, 9) | *L* (1, 5) | *S* (3, 10)  *U* (5, 11) |
| *F* (6, 9) | *M* (3, 7) *(connect to A)* | *T* (3, 11)  *V* (5, 10) |
| *G* (6, 13) | | |

**a.** Draw Mariella on grid paper.

**b.** Mariella is in the Fun House. When she passes through the Mystic Gateway, she undergoes an enlargement that makes a copy which is similar to the original Mariella. Write a rule that producers of the video game could use to enlarge Mariella. (The new image must fit on a sheet of grid paper.)

**c.** Explain how you know that the enlargement is similar to the original Mariella.

**d.** When Mariella gets caught in the Distortion Room, she is no longer similar to the original Mariella. Write a rule that would transform Mariella when she is in the Distortion Room.

**e.** How do you know that the distorted figure is not similar to the original Mariella?

**12.** Gilligan belongs to the Model Sailboat Club. All club members have *similar* boats with *similar* sails. Find all the triangles below that could be used as sails by the club members. Explain your reasoning.

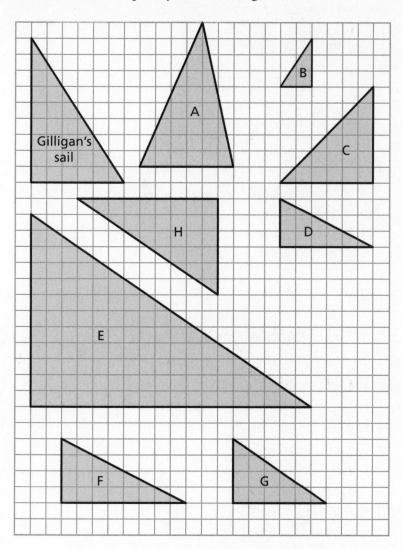

# Check-Up

**A survey of 120 players in a soccer league asked which drink they preferred during and after a game.**

| Drink | During Game | After Game |
|---|---|---|
| Sports Beverage | 70 | 10 |
| Juice | 10 | 80 |
| Water | 40 | 30 |

1. Write mathematical comparison statements about player drink preferences *during* the game.

   **a.** one statement using ratios

   **b.** one statement using percents

2. Write mathematical comparison statements about player drink preferences *after* the game.

   **a.** one statement using fractions

   **b.** one statement using differences

3. **a.** Write a ratio to describe the number of players who prefer a sports beverage to water *during* the game.

   **b.** Write an equivalent form of the ratio.

## Check-Up (continued)

4. The soccer league director makes the following statements based on the survey. Which statements are accurate? Explain.

   **a.** During the game, players prefer juice to water by a ratio of 4 to 1.

   **b.** 25% of the players prefer water after the game.

   **c.** More than half of the players prefer a sports beverage during the game.

5. So far this year, the University of North Carolina Tar Heels have won 22 games and lost 5 games.

   **a.** Suppose they continue at the same pace and lose 45 games. How many will they have won?

   **b.** What is an appropriate comparison to make between the number of games won and the number of games lost? Explain why you chose that type of comparison.

# Partner Quiz

The school newspaper club votes to have a picnic for its 30 members. The picnic planners investigate prices for food and drink at two stores and list their findings in a table.

**Food and Drink Prices**

| Item | Streamline Market | | Bulky Store | |
|---|---|---|---|---|
| | Quantity | Cost | Quantity | Cost |
| Cola | 6 cans (12 ounces each) | $1.99 | a case of twenty-four cans (12 ounces each) | $6.99 |
| Ground Beef (for hamburgers) | 1 pound (makes four hamburgers) | $1.39 | 10 patties ($\frac{1}{4}$ pound each) | $4.99 |
| Hamburger Buns | 8-count package | $1.49 | 12-count package | $2.09 |
| Potato Chips | small bag (1.5 ounces) | $0.89 | Fun Pack (eight 1.5-ounce bags) | $6.99 |

1. How much does it cost to make 30 hamburger patties with ground beef purchased from Streamline? Show your work.

2. How much do 30 hamburger patties cost at Bulky's? Show your work.

## Partner Quiz (continued)

**3.** Which store offers the better buy for cola? Explain.

**4.** The planners need to purchase enough hamburger buns to make 30 sandwiches. Buns come in packages of 8 or 12, depending on where they shop. Which store offers the better buy for the hamburger buns? How much do they cost at that store? Explain.

**5.** The meal at the picnic will include:
- one 12-ounce can of cola
- one hamburger with bun
- one small bag of potato chips (10.5 ounce bag)

The school cafeteria will donate mustard, ketchup, relish, onions, paper plates and napkins. The picnic planners will buy each item at whichever store has the better price. All 30 members of the newspaper club will attend the picnic.

How much should the students charge each person in order to cover the food expenses? Show how you determined the amount.

# Multiple-Choice Items
............................................................................................................

1. The ratio of boys to girls in a class is 2 to 3. There are 12 boys in the class. How many girls are in the class?

   **A.** 8          **B.** 18          **C.** 13          **D.** 30

2. One can of cola costs $1.25 in a vending machine. A 12-pack of the same cola costs $3.49 at the grocery store. How much money do you save by purchasing a dozen cans of cola at the grocery store instead of a dozen at the vending machine?

   **F.** $2.24          **G.** $0.96          **H.** $11.51          **J.** $12.49

3. Find the value of $x$ in the proportion.
$$\frac{6}{21} = \frac{10}{x}$$

   **A.** 35          **B.** 25          **C.** 40          **D.** 30

4. The ratio of teachers to students is 1 to 26. What is an equivalent ratio?

   **F.** 52 to 2          **G.** 11 to 36          **H.** 26 to 1          **J.** 5 to 130

5. A recipe for a fruit smoothie drink asks for strawberries and raspberries. The ratio of strawberries to raspberries in the drink is 4 to 12. What percent of the berries are strawberries?

   **A.** 33%          **B.** 25%          **C.** 66%          **D.** 75%

6. Which size ice cream dessert gives you the best price per ounce?

   **F.** Small 6-oz cup for $2.49          **G.** Medium 10-oz cup for $3.49

   **H.** Large 16-oz cup for $4.99          **J.** Super Size 24-oz cup for $7.69

# Notebook Checklist

Place a ✓ next to each item you have completed.

**Notebook Organization**

_____ Problems and Mathematical Reflections are labeled and dated.

_____ Work is neat and easy to find and follow.

**Vocabulary**

_____ All words are listed.    _____ All words are defined or described.

**Assessments**

_____ Check-Up

_____ Partner Quiz

_____ Unit Test

**Assignments**

_____ _____    _____ _____
_____ _____    _____ _____
_____ _____    _____ _____
_____ _____    _____ _____
_____ _____    _____ _____
_____ _____    _____ _____
_____ _____    _____ _____
_____ _____    _____ _____
_____ _____    _____ _____
_____ _____    _____ _____
_____ _____    _____ _____
_____ _____    _____ _____
_____ _____    _____ _____
_____ _____    _____ _____
_____ _____    _____ _____

# Self Assessment

**Mathematical Ideas**

When making comparisons, it often requires more than just finding which number is larger or smaller. It may require using ratios, rates, scaling, and proportions. After studying the mathematics in *Comparing and Scaling*:

**1. a.** I learned these things about comparing numbers in different ways:

    **b.** Here are page numbers of notebook entries that give evidence of what I have learned, along with descriptions of what each entry shows:

**2. a.** The mathematical ideas that I am still struggling with:

    **b.** This is why I think these ideas are difficult for me:

    **c.** Here are page numbers of notebook entries that give evidence of what I am struggling with, along with descriptions of what each entry shows:

**Class Participation**

I contributed to the classroom **discussion** and understanding of *Comparing and Scaling* when I . . . (Give examples.)

# Self Assessment (continued)

## Learning Environment

**Rate the learning activities using this scale:**

**1** I consistently struggled to understand the mathematics and I'm still not sure that I know it.

**2** I struggled somewhat but now I understand more than I did.

**3** I had to work, but I feel confident that I understand now.

**4** I understood everything pretty easily and I feel confident that I know the mathematics in these problems.

**5** Everything came easily. I knew most of the mathematics before we did this.

### Learning Activities

_____ Problems from the Investigations

_____ ACE Homework Assignments

_____ Mathematical Reflections

_____ Check-Up

_____ Partner Quiz

_____ Unit Test

**Check any of the following that you feel are the most helpful in adding to the success of your learning.**

❑ Working on my own in class.

❑ Discussing a problem with a partner.

❑ Working in a small group of 3 or 4 people.

❑ Discussing a problem as a whole class.

❑ Individual or group presentation to the whole class.

❑ Hearing how other people solved the problem.

❑ Summarizing the mathematics as a class and taking notes.

❑ Completing homework assignments.

# Unit Test

**1.** A sign at the fair advertises ticket prices for the carnival games.

> Red Tickets: 50 tickets for $37.50
>
> Blue Tickets: 20 tickets for $16.00
>
> Yellow Tickets: 5 tickets for $5.00

    **a.** Find the unit price for each ticket color.
    Red Tickets

    Blue Tickets

    Yellow Tickets

    **b.** How much would 40 red tickets cost?

    **c.** How many blue tickets could you buy for $20.00?

# Unit Test (continued)

2. The fair's train ride covers a distance of 3 miles in 20 minutes.

   **a.** What is the speed for the ride in miles per minute?

   **b.** What is the speed for the ride in miles per hour?

   **c.** Write an equation you can use to determine how long it would take the train to cover any distance if it travels at this same speed.

   **d.** How far does the train travel in 45 minutes?

3. There are 64 pretzels in a 16-ounce bag of chocolate covered pretzels.

   **a.** Write and solve a proportion that you can use to find the number of chocolate covered pretzels in a 5-ounce bag.

   **b.** What is the number of chocolate covered pretzels per ounce?

   **c.** How many ounces does each pretzel weigh?

# Unit Test (continued)

**4.** Kathy the Crazy Clown gives away 2,500 balloons. Her rival clown, Lazy Linda, gives away 1,600 balloons. Write two different kinds of mathematical comparison statements about the number of balloons each clown gave away.

 **i.**

 **ii.**

**5.** Kelsey makes $156.00 in two weeks at her job with the traveling carnival.

 **a.** At that rate, how much does she make in a 52-week year?

 **b.** Kelsey works 12 hours per week. How much does she make per hour?

 **c.** Kelsey is saving to buy a used car that will cost $2,200.00. How many weeks will she have to work to save enough money to buy the car?

**6.** There are two doorways into the fun house. The doors are similar rectangles. The tall door is 9 feet high and 5 feet wide. The short door is 4 feet high. How wide is the short door?

# Question Bank

Assign these questions as additional homework, or use them as review, quiz, or test questions.

For Exercises 1 and 2, use the following data about Lincoln Middle School.

> **Lincoln Middle School**
> Enrollment: 623 students
> Ratio of girls to boys: 2 to 3

1. How many girls are enrolled in Lincoln Middle School?

2. Suppose there is one teacher on staff for every 25 students enrolled. Estimate the number of teachers at Lincoln Middle School.

3. *Donuts4U* has donuts on sale at 12 for $5.40. Use division to find the unit rates that answer each question.

   a. What is the cost per donut?

   b. How many donuts can you buy for a dollar?

4. The school store sells pencils at 24 for $3.00.

   a. What are the two unit rates that you might compare?

   b. Compute each unit rate and tell what it means.

5. Find a value of $x$ that will make each proportion true.

   a. $\frac{2}{3} = \frac{x}{24}$  b. $\frac{3}{4} = \frac{18}{x}$  c. $\frac{x}{5} = \frac{4}{20}$

   d. $\frac{6}{10} = \frac{x}{15}$  e. $\frac{12}{16} = \frac{x}{20}$  f. $\frac{8}{12} = \frac{14}{x}$

6. Kaitlyn wants to estimate the number of candies in a 2-pound (32-ounce) bag of chocolate-covered peanuts. She examines several 2-ounce packages of the same candy and counts 8 or 9 candies in each.

   a. How many pieces of candy can Kaitlyn expect to get in a 2-pound bag?

   b. Kaitlyn wants to fill a 64-ounce candy bowl. The 2-ounce bags are sold 8 for $1.00, and the 32-ounce bag costs $2.79. Which is the better buy? Tell how much less it would cost to fill her bowl this way compared to filling it with packages of the other size.

**7.** Pentominoes Pizza introduces a new pizza called the Giant Foot to compete with Wee Czar's 2-pizzas-for-the-price-of-1 offer. The Giant Foot is two 1-square-foot pizzas put together. Pentominoes' ad claims that the Giant Foot is 25% larger than two Wee Czar's 12-inch round pizzas. A Giant Foot costs $8.99. Two 12-inch round pizzas from Wee Czar's cost $8.88.

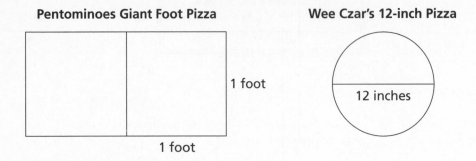

**Pentominoes Giant Foot Pizza**        1 foot

1 foot

**Wee Czar's 12-inch Pizza**        12 inches

**a.** Which offer gives you more pizza for your money?

**b.** Is the Giant Foot 25% larger than two 12-inch round pizzas from Wee Czar's? If so, prove it. If not, use percents to show how they really compare.

**8.** Which offer is the better buy?

| 2-liter bottles of Orange Splash! 4 for $4.99 | $\frac{1}{2}$-liter bottles of Orange Splash! $1.99 per 8-pack |
|---|---|

**9.** On Earth, land covers 57,900,000 square miles and water covers 139,000,000 square miles.

**a.** Write a statement comparing Earth's land surface to its water surface.

**b.** What portion of Earth's surface is water?

**c.** How does Earth's total surface area compare to your state's area?

**10.** Leticia is shopping for gifts. She compares prices at two stores so she can get the best deals. For each item, tell which store has the better price.

**Gift Prices**

| Gift | Darren's Warehouse | U-Rule Department Store |
|---|---|---|
| handkerchiefs | package of 10 for $11.00 | package of 3 for $3.75 |
| greeting cards | package of 8 for $9.99 | package of 3 for $5.49 |
| ballpoint pens | one dozen for $9.60 | 2 for $1.59 |
| audiocassette tapes | one dozen for $13.20 | 5-pack for $5.95 |

For Exercises 11–13, use the map below.

11. What would be the approximate driving time to travel from Seattle to New York at an average speed of 55 miles per hour?

12. An airplane averages 500 miles per hour. Choose two cities on the map, and find out how long would it take this plane to fly between them.

13. How far is it from your city to Chihuahua, Mexico?

For Exercises 14–17, use the data below. The table shows the all-time top 10 American movies in terms of North American Box Office earnings.

### All-Time Top 10 American Movies

| Rank | Title (year released) | Earnings (millions) |
|------|----------------------|---------------------|
| 1 | *Titanic* (1997) | $600.8 |
| 2 | *Star Wars: Episode IV–A New Hope* (1977) | $461.0 |
| 3 | *Shrek 2* (2004) | $436.7 |
| 4 | *E.T. The Extra-Terrestrial* (1982) | $435.0 |
| 5 | *Star Wars: Episode I–The Phantom Menace* (1999) | $431.1 |
| 6 | *Spider-Man* (2002) | $403.7 |
| 7 | *The Lord of the Rings: The Return of the King* (2003) | $377.0 |
| 8 | *The Passion of the Christ* (2004) | $370.3 |
| 9 | *Spider-Man 2* (2004) | $368.4 |
| 10 | *Jurassic Park* (1993) | $357.1 |
| | **Total earnings** | **$4,248.1** |

SOURCE: *Variety,* as found in *The World Almanac and Book of Facts 2005.*

**14.** How do the earnings of *Titanic* and *Jurassic Park* compare?

**15.** Write a fraction that compares the earnings between *Star Wars: Episode IV– A New Hope* to the total earnings from the top 10 movies.

**16.** Write a ratio that compares the earnings of *Titanic* to *Spider-Man*.

**17.** Write a decimal that compares the earnings of *E.T. The Extra-Terrestrial* to the total earnings from the top 10 movies.

**For Exercises 18–20, use the data in the chart, which shows the population of some counties in the United States.**

### Selected Counties With Populations Over 1 Million

| County | State | 2000 Population | 2003 Population |
|--------|-------|-----------------|-----------------|
| Los Angeles | California | 9,519,338 | 9,871,506 |
| Harris | Texas | 3,400,578 | 3,596,086 |
| Maricopa | Arizona | 3,072,149 | 3,389,260 |
| Kings | New York | 2,465,326 | 2,472,523 |
| Wayne | Michigan | 2,061,162 | 2,028,778 |
| King | Washington | 1,737,034 | 1,761,411 |
| New York | New York | 1,537,195 | 1,564,798 |
| Cuyahoga | Ohio | 1,393,978 | 1,363,888 |
| Broward | Florida | 1,623,018 | 1,731,347 |
| Allegheny | Pennsylvania | 1,281,666 | 1,261,303 |

SOURCE: Bureau of the Census

**18.** How do the populations for Los Angeles County in 2000 and 2003 compare?

**19.** Which county had the greatest increase in population from 2000 to 2003? What was the increase?

**20.** Which counties had a decrease in population from 2000 to 2003? Write the decreased amounts as percents.

**For Exercises 21–23, use these data about planets in our solar system.**

| Planet | Average Distance From the Sun (millions of miles) | Diameter at Equator (miles) | Time to Circle the Sun | Time to Turn on Axis |
|---|---|---|---|---|
| Mercury | 36 | 3,032 | 88 days | 59 days |
| Venus | 67 | 7,521 | 225 days | 243 days |
| Earth | 93 | 7,926 | 365 days | 23.9 hours |
| Mars | 142 | 4,222 | 687 days | 24.6 hours |
| Jupiter | 484 | 88,846 | 11.9 years | 9.9 hours |
| Saturn | 891 | 74,897 | 29 years | 10.7 hours |
| Uranus | 1,785 | 31,763 | 84 years | 17.2 hours |
| Neptune | 2,793 | 30,775 | 164 years | 16.1 hours |
| Pluto | 3,647 | 1,485 | 248 years | 6 days |

SOURCE: The National Space Science Data Center at NASA's Goddard Space Flight Center

21. Write a statement comparing the times taken by the various planets to circle the Sun.

22. Write a statement comparing the times taken by the planets to turn on their axes.

23. Mr. Martinelli's science class wants to make a scale model of the universe for the science fair. They need to make some calculations before building their model.

  a. The diameter of the sun is 865,000 miles. If the class made Earth's diameter = 1 inch, what would be the diameter of the scale model of the Sun?

  b. If they made Earth's diameter = 1 inch, what would be the diameter of the scale model of Jupiter?

  c. If they made Earth's diameter = 1 inch, what would be the diameter of the scale model of Pluto?

  d. If the class placed the planets by using a scale of 1 inch = 1 million miles, how many feet from the Sun would the model of Mercury have to be placed?

  e. Using the scale 1 inch = 1 million miles, how far from the Sun would the model of Earth have to be placed?

  f. Using the scale 1 inch = 1 million miles, how far from the Sun would the model of Pluto have to be placed?

# Partner Quiz

**1.** Construct a number line using the line below. Locate the numbers in parts (a)–(c) on your number line.

   **a.** ⁻8                **b.** 0                **c.** $\frac{1}{3}$

   **d.** In a different color, locate the opposite of each number in parts (a)–(c).

**2.** The school store bought supplies worth $250 to open the school year, so they started recording their account with a balance of $ ⁻250. What was their account balance after these results in September, October, November and December? Write number sentences to show your thinking.

   **a.** September → income of $175

   **b.** October → income of $200, cost of new supplies $125

   **c.** November → income of $125

   **d.** December → cost of new supplies $150, income of $60

**3.** Solve each of the computation problems below.

   **a.** ⁻15 − 7 =                     **b.** 15 + ⁻7 =

   **c.** ⁻1.5 + ⁻8.5 =               **d.** 11 − 23 =

# Partner Quiz (continued)

**4.** The table contains data for the temperature in Portland, Maine, during the
month of January. Complete the table.

**January Temperatures in Portland, Maine**

| Temperature At 8:00 A.M. | Temperature At 8:00 P.M. | Change in Temperature From 8:00 A.M. to 8 P.M. |
|---|---|---|
| −8° | 3° | |
| −2° | −13° | |
| −13° | | 11° |
| −1° | | 15° |
| | −2° | −8° |
| | −5° | 4° |

**5.** Cassidy wrote the equation $n + {}^-11 = 24$. Using what you know about fact
families, rewrite the equation so that Cassidy could figure out the value of $n$.

# Check-Up

1. A bakery bought 225 pounds of baking powder. It used 6.8 pounds per day. How much did the bakery have left after three days? Write number sentences to show your work.

2. Ray is in debt $32 right now. He had owed more, but he has been paying $6 a month on his debt for the last five months.

   **a.** How much was Ray in debt five months ago?

   **b.** At his present rate, how much longer will it take Ray to pay off his debt? Explain your reasoning.

**Solve the problems.**

3. $7 - 10 =$

4. $^-7 + 10 =$

5. $^-12 - {}^-11 =$

6. $11 - {}^-8 =$

7. $\dfrac{-\,24}{-\,6} =$

8. $25 \times {}^-6 =$

9. $^-12 \times {}^-5 =$

10. $^-27 \div 3 =$

# Multiple Choice Items
. . . . . . . . . . . . . . . . . . . . . . . . . . . . . . . . . . . . . . . . . . . . . . . . . . . . . . . . . . . . . . . . . . . . . . . . . . . . . . . . . . . . .

**1.** In which quadrant does the point $(^-9, 7)$ lie?

   **A.** I             **B.** II            **C.** III           **D.** IV

**2.** Choose the symbol that makes this number statement true.

$$-\frac{3}{4} \;\square\; {}^-0.34$$

   **F.** $>$          **G.** $=$          **H.** $<$          **J.** $\approx$

**3.** $-\frac{4}{5} + {}^-1.7 =$

   **A.** $^-5.12$       **B.** $^-2.5$       **C.** $^-0.9$       **D.** $-\frac{25}{20}$

**4.** $520 - {}^-264 =$

   **F.** 256       **G.** 344       **H.** 244       **J.** 784

**5.** $^-8 \times {}^-29 =$

   **A.** 232       **B.** $^-232$       **C.** 211       **D.** $^-211$

**6.** $^-23 \div 0.5 =$

   **F.** $^-11.5$       **G.** $^-46$       **H.** 11.5       **J.** 46

**7.** $45 - 23 \times 2 + 1 =$

   **A.** 43       **B.** $^-22$       **C.** 0       **D.** 68

**8.** Given the expression $6 \times (14 - 7)$, find the expression that is NOT equivalent.

   **F.** $(6 \times 14) - 7$                **G.** $6 \times 7$

   **H.** $(6 \times 14) - (6 \times 7)$       **J.** $(6 \times 14) + (6 \times -7)$

# Notebook Checklist

**Place a ✓ next to each item you have completed.**

### Notebook Organization

_____ Problems and Mathematical Reflections are labeled and dated.

_____ Work is neat and easy to find and follow.

### Vocabulary

_____ All words are listed.     _____ All words are defined or described.

### Assessments

_____ Check-Up

_____ Partner Quiz

_____ Unit Test

### Assignments

| | | | |
|---|---|---|---|
| _____ | _____ | _____ | _____ |
| _____ | _____ | _____ | _____ |
| _____ | _____ | _____ | _____ |
| _____ | _____ | _____ | _____ |
| _____ | _____ | _____ | _____ |
| _____ | _____ | _____ | _____ |
| _____ | _____ | _____ | _____ |
| _____ | _____ | _____ | _____ |
| _____ | _____ | _____ | _____ |
| _____ | _____ | _____ | _____ |
| _____ | _____ | _____ | _____ |
| _____ | _____ | _____ | _____ |
| _____ | _____ | _____ | _____ |

Name _____ Date _____ Class _____

# Self Assessment

# Self Assessment *(continued)*

**Learning Environment**

**Rate the learning activities using this scale:**

**1** I consistently struggled to understand the mathematics and I'm still not sure that I know it.

**2** I struggled somewhat but now I understand more than I did.

**3** I had to work, but I feel confident that I understand now.

**4** I understood everything pretty easily and I feel confident that I know the mathematics in these problems.

**5** Everything came easily. I knew most of the mathematics before we did this.

**Learning Activities:**

——— Problems from the Investigations

——— ACE Homework Assignments

——— Mathematical Reflections

——— Check-Up

——— Partner Quiz

——— Unit Test

**Check any of the following that you feel are the most helpful in adding to the success of your learning.**

❏ Working on my own in class.

❏ Discussing a problem with a partner.

❏ Working in a small group of 3 or 4 people.

❏ Discussing a problem as a whole class.

❏ Individual or group presentation to the whole class.

❏ Hearing how other people solved the problem.

❏ Summarizing the mathematics as a class and taking notes.

❏ Completing homework assignments.

# Unit Test

**1.** Rewrite these numbers in order from smallest to largest.

$$\frac{2}{5}, \quad 0, \quad -\frac{3}{2}, \quad -\frac{9}{8}, \quad \frac{8}{7}$$

**2.** Find these sums and differences.

**a.** $30 - {}^-17 =$

**b.** ${}^-17 - {}^-30 =$

**c.** ${}^-150 + 75 =$

**d.** $15 - 27 =$

**e.** ${}^-14 + {}^-15 =$

**f.** $\frac{3}{4} + {}^-\frac{1}{2} =$

**3.** Robert wrote $9 \times {}^-6 - ({}^-1 + 8)$. What is the answer to Robert's calculations?

**4. a.** Write two subtraction sentences to complete the fact family for ${}^-8 + n = 62$.

**b.** Use one of the fact family sentences to find the value of $n$.

**5.** Find these products and quotients.

**a.** $13 \times {}^-7 =$

**b.** ${}^-8 \times {}^-20 =$

**c.** $99 \div {}^-3 =$

**d.** $\frac{-36}{-12} =$

**e.** $0 \div 18 =$

**f.** $\frac{1}{3} \times \frac{-5}{7} =$

**6.** Malique wants to take four of her friends to a movie. She knows it is $5.50 for a ticket and $3.25 for popcorn.

    **a.** How much will it cost if she pays for the movie and popcorn for all five people?

    **b.** Write a number sentence to show how you computed the total cost.

    **c.** Find a different way to calculate the total cost and show it in a number sentence.

**7.** Insert = or ≠ to make the statements true.

    **a.** $11 + {}^-20 \ \square \ {}^-20 + 11$          **b.** $12 - {}^-10 \ \square \ {}^-10 - 12$

    **c.** ${}^-5 \times 2 \ \square \ 2 \times {}^-5$            **d.** ${}^-16 \div {}^-4 \ \square \ {}^-4 \div {}^-16$

**8.** Plot the following points on the grid and label each point.

    **a.** $(1, {}^-5)$          **b.** $(2, 0)$          **c.** $({}^-3, 5)$

    **d.** $(0, {}^-2)$          **e.** $({}^-2, {}^-2)$

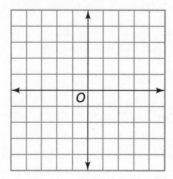

## Unit Test (continued)
...........................................................................................................

9. The list below gives monthly average low temperatures (in degrees Fahrenheit) for International Falls, Minnesota from November through March).

**Average Low Temperatures (°F) in International Falls, Minnesota**

| November | December | January | February | March |
|----------|----------|---------|----------|-------|
| 17 | 0 | −9 | −3 | 10 |

   **a.** What is the mean of these monthly low temperatures? Show your work.

   **b.** What is the difference between the highest and lowest temperatures?

In the fifteenth century, European flour merchants used positive and negative numbers. If the merchants wrote +5 on a flour barrel, it meant that the barrel was 5 pounds overweight; -5 meant that a barrel was 5 pounds underweight.

1. Suppose five 100-pound flour barrels are labeled as shown below.

   **a.** Do the five barrels contain more or less than 500 pounds altogether?

   **b.** How much more or less?

2. Suppose these numbers are on eight 100-pound barrels:

$$^-6 \quad {}^-8 \quad {}^+7 \quad {}^+2 \quad {}^-10 \quad {}^+6 \quad {}^+3 \quad {}^+1$$

   **a.** Do the barrels contain more or less than 800 pounds altogether?

   **b.** How much more or less?

3. The drawings below show six 100-pound barrels. The total weight in the barrels is 11 pounds under 600 pounds. Suppose each barrel is marked with a different number. Show a way that the barrels could be marked. Keep your numbers between $^-10$ and $^+10$.

4. Terri made up a game of darts for a party. To play the game, you throw three darts at the board and then total your points. The highest score wins. List all possible scores for three darts if all three hit the target.

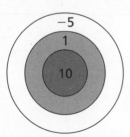

**Answer Questions 5–8 with "true" or "false," and *explain* your answer.**

5. The sum of two negative integers is always negative.

6. The product of two negative integers is always negative.

7. The sum of a negative integer and a positive integer is always positive.

8. The product of a negative integer and a positive integer is always negative.

9. One integer added to another integer gives a sum of ⁻9. When the smaller integer is subtracted from the greater integer, the difference is 1. What could the two integers be?

10. **a.** Below is a grid with four quadrants. Plot the following points, and connect them with line segments.

   Point A  (1, 0)          Point B  (3, 4)          Point C  (4, 0)

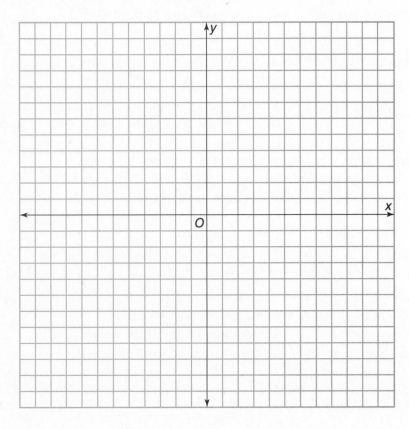

**b.** On the same grid paper, transform your figure $ABC$ using the rule $(2x, 2y)$.

**c.** On the same grid paper, transform your figure $ABC$ using the rule $(^-2x, ^-2y)$.

**d.** On the same grid paper, transform your figure $ABC$ using the rule $(^-2x, 2y)$.

**e.** On the same grid paper, transform your figure $ABC$ using the rule $(2x, ^-2y)$.

**f.** Without drawing, predict what will happen to $ABC$ using the rule $(3x, 3y)$.

**g.** Without drawing, predict what will happen to $ABC$ using the rule $(^-3x, ^-3y)$.

**h.** Without drawing, predict what will happen to $ABC$ using the rule $(^-3x, 3y)$.

**11.** Rewrite these temperature readings from lowest to highest.

$^-9°$    $14°$    $^-2°$    $0°$    $8°$    $^-1°$    $1°$

**12. a.** Suppose the temperature is $6°$. What will the temperature be if it rises $22°$?

**b.** Suppose the temperature is $6°$. What will the temperature be if it falls $7°$?

**13. a.** Suppose the temperature is $^-6°$ ($6°$ below $0°$). What will the temperature be if it rises $13°$?

**b.** Suppose the temperature is $^-6°$. What will the temperature be if it falls $15°$?

**14.** Barry plays fullback on his high school football team. Sometimes he gains yardage ($^+5$ means a 5-yard gain). Sometimes he loses yardage ($^-3$ means a 3-yard loss). Determine Barry's total yardage in each game below.

**a.** Game 1: $^+4$    $^+6$    $^+7$    $^+1$    $^-8$

**b.** Game 2: $^+6$    $^-3$    $0$    $^+15$    $^-1$    $^+8$    $^+11$    $^-6$

**15.** Suppose the Rocky Mountains have 72 centimeters of snow. Warmer weather is melting the snow at a rate of 5.8 centimeters a day. If the snow continues to melt at this rate, after seven days of warm weather, how much snow will be left?

**16.** Write a number less than $^-1000$.

# Question Bank (continued)

**17.** After several minutes of playing MathMania, three teams have the following scores:

| SuperSmarties | DynaBrains | MegaMinds |
|---|---|---|
| 650 | $^-150$ | 200 |

**a.** The SuperSmarties are how many points ahead of MegaMinds? Write a number sentence that could be used to find this amount.

**b.** The SuperSmarties are how many points ahead of DynaBrains? Write a number sentence that could be used to find this amount.

**c.** The MegaMinds are how many points ahead of DynaBrains? Write a number sentence that could be used to find this amount.

**Tell how far apart the two numbers are on a number line.**

**18.** $^-15$ and $^+20$      **19.** 37 and 17      **20.** $^-5$ and $^+12$

**Solve the problem.**

**21.** $18 - 27 = \square$          **22.** $27 - 18 = \square$

**23.** $14 - {}^-8 = \square$          **24.** $^-14 - {}^+8 = \square$

**25.** $^-150 - {}^+24 = \square$          **26.** $90 - {}^-99 = \square$

**27.** $16 + 12 + {}^-4 = \square$          **28.** $\square + 21 = 13$

**29.** The temperature for the past 8 hours has been changing at the rate of $^-1.5°$ each hour. The meteorologist predicts that the temperature will continue changing like this for the next 6 hours. The present reading is 0°.

**a.** What was the temperature reading 7 hours ago?

**b.** What temperature is predicted for 6 hours from now?

**c.** When was the temperature reading 6°?

**d.** When is the temperature expected to be $^-8°$?

**30.** Use this information: Suppose you are in a building in which the floors are numbered from 0 to 15. The building has an underground parking garage with 10 levels, which are numbered from ⁻1 to ⁻10. Which floor is *farther from* floor ⁻2? (Drawing a picture may help you solve this problem.)

    **a.** floor 7 or floor ⁻10

    **b.** floor 2 or floor ⁻8

    **c.** floor 1 or floor ⁻5

**31.** A bakery bought 225 pounds of baking powder. It used 6.8 pounds per day. How much did the bakery have left after three days?

**32.** Ray is in debt $32. He was further in debt, but he has been paying $6 a month on his debt for the last five months.

    **a.** How much was Ray in debt five months ago?

    **b.** At his present rate, how much longer will it take Ray to pay off his debt? Explain your reasoning.

**33.** Find the answers of the following number sentences.

    **a.** $(5 + {}^-3) \times 4 - 2$

    **b.** $3^2 \times {}^-7 + 2$

    **c.** $4 - 4 \times 2 + 2 \times {}^-1$

    **d.** ${}^-2 \times (3 + {}^-10) - 2^2$

    **e.** $10 - (50 \div ({}^-2 \times 25) + 7) \times 2^2$

**34.** Use the Distributive Property to write an expression equal to each of the following. Solve for parts (a) and (b) and simplify the expression in part (c).

    **a.** ${}^-2 \bullet ({}^-8 + 5)$

    **b.** $({}^-7 \bullet {}^-2) - ({}^-7 \bullet {}^-12)$

    **c.** $x \bullet (9 + {}^-5)$

# Question Bank (continued)

**35.** In the school's Future Investors Club stock market game, the following gains/losses in stock price were earned over 10 days.

**Stock Market Game**

| Day | 1 | 2 | 3 | 4 | 5 | 6 | 7 | 8 | 9 | 10 |
|---|---|---|---|---|---|---|---|---|---|---|
| Gain/Loss | −$5.50 | $0 | −$3.50 | $3 | $4 | −$0.50 | $1 | −$2 | −$2.40 | −$3 |

Companies often plot stock price gains/losses to display the changes over time. Plot a graph of the (day, gain/loss) data for the Future Investors Club.

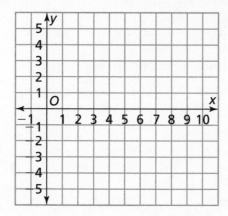

**36.** Use the Distributive Property to write each of these calculations in an equivalent form.

**a.** $(56 \times 115) + (56 \times {}^{-}15)$

**b.** $10 \times ({}^{-}6 - 3)$

# Check-Up 1

**1. a.** Which of the following tables represent linear relationships?

**Table 1**

| x | y |
|---|---|
| 0 | 5 |
| 1 | 10 |
| 2 | 12 |
| 3 | 16 |
| 4 | 20 |

**Table 2**

| x | y |
|---|---|
| 0 | 0 |
| 1 | 10 |
| 2 | 20 |
| 3 | 30 |
| 4 | 40 |

**Table 3**

| x | y |
|---|---|
| 0 | 10 |
| 1 | 8 |
| 2 | 6 |
| 3 | 4 |
| 4 | 2 |

**b.** Write an equation for each table of linear relationships in part (a).

**2.** Each equation below represents a linear relationship between *x* and *y*. For each equation, describe what happens to the *y* value as the *x* value increases by 1.

**a.** $y = x + 50$

**b.** $y = -5x + 10$

## Check-Up 1 (continued)

**3.** Each graph below represents a linear relationship between *x* and *y*. For each graph, describe what happens to the *y* value as the *x* value increases by 1.

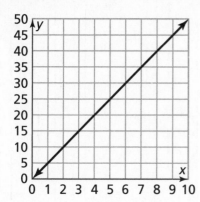 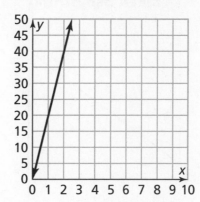

**4.** Does the table below represent a linear relationship? Explain your reasoning.

| x | y |
|---|---|
| 0 | 100 |
| 2 | 130 |
| 6 | 190 |
| 8 | 220 |
| 9 | 235 |

# Partner Quiz

**1.** This is a graph of money earned by Jake while babysitting for several hours.

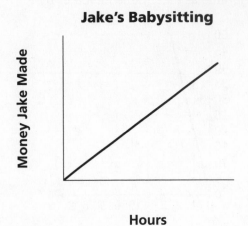

**Jake's Babysitting**

*(y-axis: Money Jake Made)*

*(x-axis: Hours)*

**a.** Put a scale on the axes that makes sense for this situation. Explain why you chose your scale.

**b.** Write an equation for the graph based on the scale you chose in part (a).

**c.** If the line on this graph was steeper, what would it tell about the money Jake is making? Write an equation for such a line.

## Partner Quiz (continued)

2. Rachael's backyard swimming pool is being emptied by a pump. The amount of water in the pool ($W$, measured in gallons) at any time ($t$, measured in hours) is given by the following equation:

$$W = -250t + 9000$$

   **a.** How many gallons of water are being pumped out each hour? Explain.

   **b.** After 11 hours how much water is left in the pool? Explain.

   **c.** How much water was in the pool at the start? Explain.

   **d.** How long will it take the pool to empty? Explain.

3. Jabal and Michael agree to leave their homes at the same time and meet somewhere in between their houses. Jabal leaves his house walking 2 meters per second. Michael leaves his house walking at 2.5 meters per second. If their homes are 20 meters apart, how far from Jabal's house will they meet? How long did each walk? Show all your work.

# Check-Up 2

**1.** Find the value of the indicated variable.

    **a.** Suppose $y = 2x + 10$. Find $y$ if $x = -2$.

    **b.** Suppose $y = 2x - 2.5$. Find $x$ if $y = 10$.

**2.** Solve each equation to find the value of $x$.

    **a.** $4x + 10 = 22$

    **b.** $3x + 9 = 6x$

    **c.** $2(x + 3) = 18$

    **d.** $2x + 15 = 27 - 4x$

## Check-Up 2 *(continued)*

**3.** The pep club is going to sell bouquets of flowers during the homecoming game. They represent their revenue $R$ and costs $C$ with the following equations.

$$R = 5.50x \qquad\qquad C = 250 + 1.25x \qquad\qquad x \text{ is the number of bouquets.}$$

**a.** When is the pep club's revenue equal to their costs? Explain.

**b.** What is the $y$-intercept of the line for each equation? What information does it represent in this context?

**c.** What is the constant rate of change for each relationship? What information does it represent in this context?

Name _____ Date _____ Class _____

# Multiple-Choice Items
...............................................................................................................................................

1. Which of the following data sets is linear?

A.

| x | 3 | 4 | 5 | 6 |
|---|---|---|---|---|
| y | 5 | 7 | 10 | 15 |

B.

| x | 3 | 4 | 5 | 6 |
|---|---|---|---|---|
| y | 6 | 9 | 12 | 15 |

C.

| x | 3 | 4 | 5 | 6 |
|---|---|---|---|---|
| y | 9 | 16 | 25 | 36 |

D.

| x | 3 | 4 | 5 | 6 |
|---|---|---|---|---|
| y | 3 | 9 | 27 | 81 |

2. Which of the following is linear?

    **F.** $y = 2 + 3x$     **G.** $y = 2x(x + 5)$     **H.** $y = 4x^2$     **J.** $y = 2^x$

3. The following data represents a linear relationship. What is the slope of the line that represents the data?

| x | 1 | 2 | 3 | 4 |
|---|---|---|---|---|
| y | 4 | 7 | 10 | 13 |

    **A.** 4         **B.** 3         **C.** 1         **D.** 9

4. What is the $y$-intercept of the line that represents the data in Question 3?

    **F.** 4         **G.** 3         **H.** 1         **J.** 13

5. What is the equation that represents the data set in Question 3?

    **A.** $y = x + 3$     **B.** $y = 4x + 1$     **C.** $y = 3x + 1$     **D.** $y = 3x + 13$

6. Consider the equation $y = 4x - 10$. Find $y$ if $x = 3$.

    **F.** 33         **G.** 12         **H.** 2         **J.** ⁻3

7. What is the equation of the line that contains the points $(2, 13)$ and $(6, 33)$?

    **A.** $y = \frac{1}{3}x + 3$     **B.** $y = 5x + 5$     **C.** $y = \frac{1}{3}x + 5$     **D.** $y = 5x + 3$

# Notebook Checklist

**Place a ✓ next to each item you have completed.**

## Notebook Organization

_____ Problems and Mathematical Reflections are labeled and dated.

_____ Work is neat and easy to find and follow.

## Vocabulary

_____ All words are listed.      _____ All words are defined or described.

## Assessments

_____ Check-Up 1          _____ Check-Up 2

_____ Partner Quiz        _____ Unit Test

## Assignments

_____ _____      _____ _____

_____ _____      _____ _____

_____ _____      _____ _____

_____ _____      _____ _____

_____ _____      _____ _____

_____ _____      _____ _____

_____ _____      _____ _____

_____ _____      _____ _____

_____ _____      _____ _____

_____ _____      _____ _____

_____ _____      _____ _____

_____ _____      _____ _____

_____ _____      _____ _____

_____ _____      _____ _____

_____ _____      _____ _____

# Self Assessment

**Mathematical Ideas**

After studying the mathematics in *Moving Straight Ahead*:

**1. a.** I learned these things about how linear relationships in tables, graphs and equations are displayed:

**b.** Here are page numbers of notebook entries that give evidence of what I have learned, along with descriptions of what each entry shows:

**2. a.** The mathematical ideas that I am still struggling with:

**b.** This is why I think these ideas are difficult for me:

**c.** Here are page numbers of notebook entries that give evidence of what I am struggling with, along with descriptions of what each entry shows:

**Class Participation**

I contributed to the classroom **discussion** and understanding of *Moving Straight Ahead* when I . . . (Give examples.)

# Self Assessment (continued)

**Learning Environment**

**Rate the learning activities using this scale:**

**1** I consistently struggled to understand the mathematics and I'm still not sure that I know it.

**2** I struggled somewhat but now I understand more than I did.

**3** I had to work, but I feel confident that I understand now.

**4** I understood everything pretty easily and I feel confident that I know the mathematics in these problems.

**5** Everything came easily. I knew most of the mathematics before we did this.

**Learning Activities:**

_____ Problems from the Investigations

_____ ACE Homework Assignments

_____ Mathematical Reflections

_____ Check-Ups

_____ Partner Quiz

_____ Unit Test

**Check any of the following that you feel are the most helpful in adding to the success of your learning.**

❑ Working on my own in class.

❑ Discussing a problem with a partner.

❑ Working in a small group of 3 or 4 people.

❑ Discussing a problem as a whole class.

❑ Individual or group presentation to the whole class.

❑ Hearing how other people solved the problem.

❑ Summarizing the mathematics as a class and taking notes.

❑ Completing homework assignments.

# Unit Test

**1. a.** Does it make a difference what two points you choose on a straight line to find the slope of the line? Use the line below in part (b) to help explain your answer.

**b.** Write an equation for the line below.

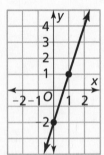

# Unit Test (continued)

2. Match a table (A–D) with a graph (E–H) and an equation (J–M). List your results below in four groups. For example, on the line for group 1 you should put 3 letters, one for a table, one for a graph, and one for an equation, which all represent the same linear pattern.

Group 1:

Group 2:

Group 3:

Group 4:

**A.**

| x | y |
|---|---|
| −2 | −5 |
| −1 | −3 |
| 0 | −1 |
| 1 | 1 |
| 2 | 3 |

**B.**

| x | y |
|---|---|
| −2 | 3 |
| −1 | 2 |
| 0 | 1 |
| 1 | 0 |
| 2 | −1 |

**C.**

| x | y |
|---|---|
| −2 | 1.5 |
| −1 | 1.5 |
| 0 | 1.5 |
| 1 | 1.5 |
| 2 | 1.5 |

**D.**

| x | y |
|---|---|
| −2 | −3 |
| −1 | −1 |
| 0 | 1 |
| 1 | 3 |
| 2 | 5 |

**E.**
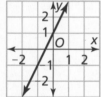

**F.**
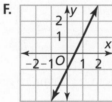

**G.**
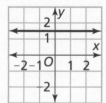

**H.**
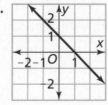

**J.** $y = 1.5$        **K.** $y = 2x - 1$        **L.** $y = 2x + 1$        **M.** $y = -x + 1$

# Unit Test (continued)
························································································································

**3.** Solve the following equations for $x$.

   **a.** $12 - 5x = 7x$

   **b.** $2x - 3 = 5x + 12$

   **c.** $2x + 25 = 7x$

   **d.** $3(x + 1) = 12$

**4.** A student, who is studying walking rates, enters the rule $y = 40 + 2x$ into the calculator and produces this graph. He has highlighted one point on the graph.

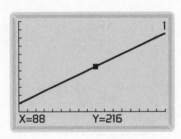

   **a.** What question could the student be trying to answer by using the graph?

   **b.** Write the question for part (a) as an equation that could be used to find the answer.

# Unit Test *(continued)*

**5.** To encourage customers, a new movie theater is offering memberships. The membership costs $75 a year plus $2 per movie. For non-members, the cost of a movie is $5.75.

    **a.** Make a table that shows the number of movies $N$ and the cost for members ($C_1$) and non-members ($C_2$).

    **b.** On the same set of axes, graph the relationship of cost and number of movies for members and non-members.

    **c.** Write an equation that shows the number of movies $N$ and the cost for members ($C_1$) and non-members ($C_2$).

    **d.** What is the slope of each line of the equations in part (c)?

    **e.** What information does the slope of each line represent in this context?

    **f.** Explain how you could find slope from a table. A graph? An equation?

    **g.** What information does the $y$-intercept of each line represent in this context?

# Question Bank

1. Brent's Video Shack charges $1.50 to rent a video game for a night. Mr. Buck's Entertainments opens a new store in town, charging $1.00 per night for a game, and starts to take customers away from Brent's Video Shack.

   **a.** Graph each price scheme on the same set of axes.

   **b.** How could Brent change his charges, so that he includes a one-time membership fee and drops his rental fee below Mr. Buck's, to get his customers back without losing too much money? Graph your proposal and explain to Brent how it will work.

2. Big A's Bike Rentals charges $300 plus $20 per bike to rent bikes for a week. Little Cheeper's rental shop charges $50 plus $35 per bike for a week. You need to determine which company to use for your bike-touring project. Write an explanation to a student who has never used a graphing calculator to help that student display and solve this problem on a graphing calculator.

3. Gretchen was absent when the class developed strategies for solving linear equations. Write an explanation to her about how to solve equations using the symbolic method. Use the equation $4n - 17 = 43$ as an example.

4. **a.** This table shows two points that are on the same straight line. Complete the table to show three other points on the same line.

   | x | −3 | | | 1 |
   |---|----|----|----|---|
   | y | −2 | | | 6 |

   **b.** Find the slope and the y-intercept of this line that represents the data.

5. Given one of the representations below, find the other two.

| Table | Graph | Equation |
|---|---|---|
| <br> x \| y <br> −2 \| 14 <br> 0 \| 8 <br> 1 \| 5 <br> 2 \| 2 <br> 3 \| −1 | | |
| | | |
| | | $y = \frac{1}{3}x + 1$ |

a. Find the *y*-intercept for each representation above.

b. Find the slope for each representation above.

6. Sam made up a set of tables based on some equations. He gave the tables to Adrian and challenged her to find the equations for each table. Adrian added two columns to each table to help her find the equations. Adrian used the extra columns to find the differences in x-values and y-values. Below is the start of her work.

**Table A**

| Diff. x | x | y | Diff. y |
|---|---|---|---|
| None | −2 | −1 | |
| 1 | −1 | 1 | 2 |
| | 0 | 3 | |
| | 1 | 5 | |
| | 2 | 7 | |

**Table B**

| Diff. x | x | y | Diff. y |
|---|---|---|---|
| | −3 | −8 | |
| | −1 | 0 | |
| | 1 | 0 | |
| 2 | 3 | −8 | |
| | 5 | −24 | |

**Table C**

| Diff. x | x | y | Diff. y |
|---|---|---|---|
| | −3 | $-\frac{1}{2}$ | |
| | −1 | $\frac{1}{2}$ | 1 |
| | 0 | 1 | |
| | 3 | 2.5 | |
| | 5 | 3.5 | |

**Table D**

| Diff. x | x | y | Diff. y |
|---|---|---|---|
| | −2 | −5 | |
| | −1 | −3 | |
| | 0 | −1 | |
| | 1 | 1 | 2 |
| | 2 | 3 | |

a. Complete these columns for each table.

b. Describe any patterns you see in the columns of differences.

c. Find the equation of any linear relationship represented in these tables.

d. Explain why Adrian added the columns to the tables Sam gave her. Do you think it helped her to find the equations? Explain your thinking.

7. The formula relating n (the number of cricket chirps per minute) to t (the temperature in degrees Fahrenheit) is $n = 4t - 160$.

a. Using a symbolic method, find how many times a cricket would chirp in a minute at 90°F.

b. It is evening, and a cricket is chirping 48 times per minute. Use a symbolic method to find the temperature.

# Check-Up 1

**1.** This net can be folded on the dashed lines to make a box.

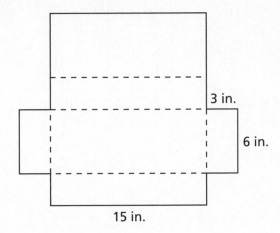

3 in.

6 in.

15 in.

  **a.** What is the surface area of the box?

  **b.** What is the volume of the box?

**2.** Pool-You-Over, a pool table supply company, is making a cardboard box to package new cubes of pool cue chalk. Each piece of chalk is 1 cubic inch. They considered all the ways to arrange 16 cubes of the chalk.

  • 16 inches by 1 inch by 1 inch

  • 8 inches by 2 inches by 1 inch

  • 4 inches by 4 inches by 1 inch

  • 4 inches by 2 inches by 2 inches

  **a.** Which arrangement of chalk would require the most cardboard for the box?

  **b.** Which arrangement of chalk would require the least cardboard for the box?

## Check-Up 1 (continued)

**3. a.** On grid paper, draw a net for a box whose dimensions are 1 by 2 by 4.

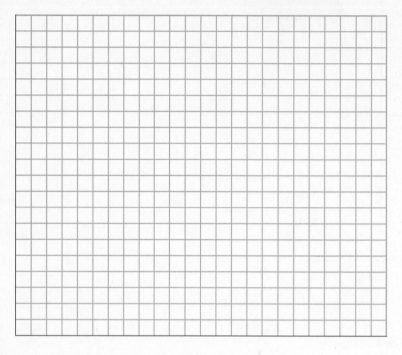

**b.** What is the volume of the box? Show your work.

**c.** What is the surface area of the box? Show your work.

# Partner Quiz

Goop and Gunk, Inc. sells oil, grease, and other compounds. Cleaning
compound can be purchased in 2 sizes of cylindrical containers, a small size for
the home and a large size for businesses.

The home size can has a radius of 2.75 inches and a height
of 8.25 inches. The business size can has a radius of
11 inches and a height of 33 inches.

1. How many square inches of aluminum are needed
   to make the home size can? (Assume the cans have
   flat bottoms and tops.)

2.75 in.

8.25 in.

11 in.

33 in.

2. How many square inches of aluminum are needed to make the
   business size can?

3. How many cubic inches of cleaning compound will the home size can hold?

4. How many cubic inches of cleaning compound will the business size can hold?

5. If a home size can sells for $0.85, what should the price of the business size can
   be if the company wants to base the price on the amount of cleaning
   compound the can will hold?

6. Goop and Gunk, Inc. is also planning to package their home size cleaning
   compound in a triangular prism. They want the triangular prism to hold the
   same amount of cleaning compound as the regular can. Give the dimensions
   of a triangular prism that will hold the same amount.

# Check-Up 2

The Student Government sells juice at school athletic events. They have been using cylinder-shaped containers with a 2-inch radius and an 8-inch height. Their supplier has suggested that they could also sell juice in cone-shaped containers with the same dimensions.

1. How much juice will the cylinder-shaped container hold if it is filled to the rim?

2. How much juice will the cone-shaped container hold if it is filled to the rim?

3. What is the difference between the amount the cylinder will hold and the amount the cone will hold?

4. The Student Government wants to use the new container. They want to give customers the same value for their money. They used to charge $1.00 for the cylinder-shaped container filled with juice. What price should they charge for the cone-shaped container?

5. The Student Government decides they also want to sell juice in new drink containers that look like basketballs. The containers have a 3.5 centimeter radius. How much juice, in cubic centimeters, will each container hold?

Name _____ Date _____ Class _____

# Multiple-Choice Items

**1.** Which net below correctly illustrates the surface area of a cylinder?

**A.**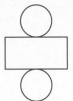

**B.**

**C.**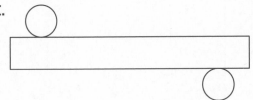

**D.**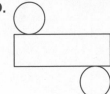

**2.** What is the surface area of the can of soup?

2.5 cm

Glop-pea Soup

8 cm

   **F.** 157.07 cm$^2$    **G.** 628.32 cm$^2$    **H.** 164.93 cm$^2$    **J.** 282.74 cm$^2$

**3.** A cone has a base that is $12\frac{1}{2}$ cm$^2$ and a height of 10 cm. What is the volume?

   **A.** 125 cm$^3$    **B.** $41\frac{2}{3}$ cm$^3$    **C.** $83\frac{1}{3}$ cm$^3$    **D.** $62\frac{1}{2}$ cm$^3$

**4.** A rectangular prism has a volume of 154 in$^3$. Which set of dimensions below could be the dimensions of the prism?

   **F.** 6 by 8 by 3    **G.** 5 by 6 by 7    **H.** 2 by 7 by 11    **J.** 3 by 8 by 9

## Multiple-Choice Items (continued)

5. Hillary is moving. She has many different boxes in which to pack her stuff. How many times greater is the volume of the larger box compared to the volume of the smaller box?

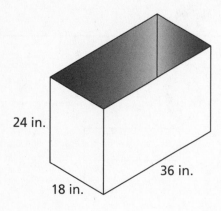
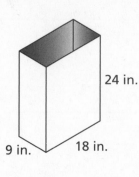

24 in.    36 in.    18 in.    24 in.    9 in.    18 in.

   **A.** 8            **B.** 4            **C.** 15,552            **D.** 3,888

6. What is the approximate volume of a sphere with a diameter of 4 centimeters?

   **F.** 268 cm$^3$        **G.** 134 cm$^3$        **H.** 75 cm$^3$        **J.** 33.5 cm$^3$

7. A box of cereal has a volume of 384 cubic inches. If the width of the box is 4 inches and the length is 8 inches, what is the height of the box?

   **A.** 6 in.        **B.** 7 in.        **C.** 12 in.        **D.** 8 in.

8. A cylindrical pop can is 12.5 centimeters tall and 5.5 centimeters wide. What is the volume of the pop can?

   **F.** 1187.91 cm$^3$  **G.** 88.36 cm$^3$        **H.** 215.98 cm$^3$        **J.** 296.98 cm$^3$

9. Annie wants to paint her living room walls blue. The room is 26 feet by 22 feet by 8 feet high. How many cans of paint will she need if each gallon covers 88 square feet (ignore doors and windows)?

   **A.** 6 cans        **B.** 9 cans        **C.** 8 cans        **D.** 5 cans

10. Maurice's family put a pool into their backyard. It is rectangular in shape and its dimensions are 20 feet by 10 feet by 10 feet. It costs $0.05 per cubic foot to fill the pool. How much will it cost Maurice's family to fill their new pool?

   **F.** $100        **G.** $200        **H.** $150        **J.** $50

# Notebook Checklist

**Place a ✓ next to each item you have completed.**

## Notebook Organization

_____ Problems and Mathematical Reflections are labeled and dated.

_____ Work is neat and easy to find and follow.

## Vocabulary

_____ All words are listed.      _____ All words are defined or described.

## Assessments

_____ Check-Up 1          _____ Check-Up 2

_____ Partner Quiz        _____ Unit Test

## Assignments

| | | | |
|---|---|---|---|
| _____ | _____ | _____ | _____ |
| _____ | _____ | _____ | _____ |
| _____ | _____ | _____ | _____ |
| _____ | _____ | _____ | _____ |
| _____ | _____ | _____ | _____ |
| _____ | _____ | _____ | _____ |
| _____ | _____ | _____ | _____ |
| _____ | _____ | _____ | _____ |
| _____ | _____ | _____ | _____ |
| _____ | _____ | _____ | _____ |
| _____ | _____ | _____ | _____ |
| _____ | _____ | _____ | _____ |
| _____ | _____ | _____ | _____ |
| _____ | _____ | _____ | _____ |
| _____ | _____ | _____ | _____ |
| _____ | _____ | _____ | _____ |

# Self Assessment

**Mathematical Ideas**

After studying the mathematics in *Filling and Wrapping:*

**1. a.** I learned these things about volume and surface area:

**b.** Here are page numbers of notebook entries that give evidence of what I have learned, along with descriptions of what each entry shows:

**2. a.** The mathematical ideas that I am still struggling with:

**b.** This is why I think these ideas are difficult for me:

**c.** Here are page numbers of notebook entries that give evidence of what I am struggling with, along with descriptions of what each entry shows:

**Class Participation**

I contributed to the classroom **discussion** and understanding of *Filling and Wrapping* when I . . . (Give examples.)

# Self Assessment *(continued)*

**Learning Environment**

**Rate the learning activities using this scale:**

**1** I consistently struggled to understand the mathematics and I'm still not sure that I know it.

**2** I struggled somewhat but now I understand more than I did.

**3** I had to work, but I feel confident that I understand now.

**4** I understood everything pretty easily and I feel confident that I know the mathematics in these problems.

**5** Everything came easily. I knew most of the mathematics before we did this.

**Learning Activities:**

\_\_\_\_ Problems from the Investigations

\_\_\_\_ ACE Homework Assignments

\_\_\_\_ Mathematical Reflections

\_\_\_\_ Check-Ups

\_\_\_\_ Partner Quiz

\_\_\_\_ Unit Test

**Check any of the following that you feel are the most helpful in adding to the success of your learning.**

❏ Working on my own in class.

❏ Discussing a problem with a partner.

❏ Working in a small group of 3 or 4 people.

❏ Discussing a problem as a whole class.

❏ Individual or group presentation to the whole class.

❏ Hearing how other people solved the problem.

❏ Summarizing the mathematics as a class and taking notes.

❏ Completing homework assignments.

# Unit Test

The Apple Theater concession sells two sizes of popcorn—a micro box and a jumbo box. Answer Exercises 1–6, and remember to show enough work so that someone reading your paper will know how you found your answers.

MICRO  6 in.
2 in.  4 in.

JUMBO  12 in.
4 in.  8 in.

1. About how many square inches of cardboard are needed to make the micro box? (There is no top on the box.)

2. About how many square inches of cardboard are needed to make the jumbo box? (There is no top on the box.)

3. What is the volume of the micro box?

4. What is the volume of the jumbo box?

5. Suppose the micro box sells for $0.75. What should the price of the jumbo box be if it is based on the amount the box holds?

6. Suppose the theater decides to have a third popcorn size, the super mongo box. They want the super mongo box to have twice the volume of the jumbo box. What dimensions could the super mongo box have?

# Unit Test (continued)

7. Jose filled a square prism with 729 cubic centimeters of colored water. He pushed a square pyramid with the same base and height as the prism into the prism and some of the water came out. How many cubic centimeters of water would be left inside the prism?

8. These are scale drawings of two cylinders. One cylinder has a radius of 6 centimeters and a height of 5 centimeters. The other cylinder has a radius of 3 centimeters and a height of 20 centimeters.

   a. Do the cylinders have the same volume? Show your calculations.

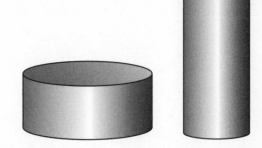

   b. Do the cylinders have the same surface area? Show your calculations.

9. This is a sketch of the nose cone of the delivery system for a new satellite. Find its volume.

8 ft

8 ft

diameter of base = 10 ft

# Question Bank

1. Could each of the nets below be folded along the lines to form a box? If yes, explain how. If no, explain why not.

   **a.**
   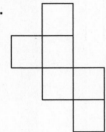

   **b.**

   **c.**

   **d.**

2. **a.** Ian said the two triangular prisms below could be placed together to form a square prism. Is Ian correct? If yes, explain how. If no, explain why not.

   2 in.    2 in.

   2 in.    2 in.

   **b.** Ian also said the surface area of this square prism is the sum of the surface areas of the two triangular prisms. Is Ian correct? If yes, explain how. If no, explain why not.

**3.** There are eight identical cubes. Each computation below is the volume or surface area of a rectangular prism that is formed by the eight cubes. Indicate if this calculation is for the volume or the surface area. Perform each computation. Find the dimensions of the box.

   **a.** $8 \times 4 + 2$

   **b.** $2 \times 2 \times 2$

   **c.** $2 \times 1 \times 4$

   **d.** $2 \times 4 + 2 \times 4 \times 2 + 2 \times 2$

**4.** Billy used three toy prisms, a cylinder, and a half sphere to build a house and a barn as below.

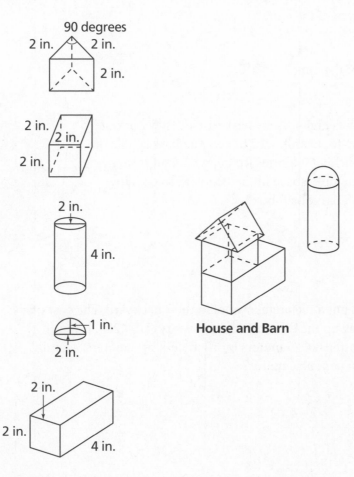

**House and Barn**

   **a.** What is the combined volume of the house and the barn?

   **b.** What is the surface area of the house?

**5.** Use the house and barn from Exercise 4 to answer the following questions.

   **a.** Given 1 inch = 2.54 centimeters. What is the volume of an inch cube in cubic centimeters?

   **b.** What is the volume of the house in cubic centimeters?

   **c.** Given 1 inch = 2.54 centimeters. What is the surface area of an inch cube in square centimeters?

   **d.** What is the surface area of the house in square centimeters?

**6.** One face of a cube has an area of 25 square centimeters.

   **a.** What is the surface area of the cube?

   **b.** What is the volume of the cube?

**7.** Sterling Sports manufactures high-quality basketballs. They package their basketballs in 1-cubic-foot cardboard boxes. The basketballs fit nicely in the boxes, just touching the sides. To keep the ball from being damaged, Sterling fills the empty space in the box with foam. How much foam is put into each basketball box?

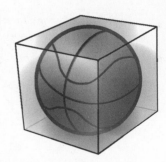

**8.** The Spitzleys are going to put a rectangular pool in their backyard. The cost of excavating the dirt (digging up the dirt and taking it away) is $4,200. If the hole that is dug has dimensions of 25 meters by 15 meters by 3 meters, what is the cost for the excavation per cubic meter?

**9. a.** Make a sketch of a rectangular box with a base of 3 feet by 5 feet and a height of 7 feet. How many unit cubes would fit in a single layer at the bottom of the box?

**b.** How many identical layers of unit cubes could be stacked in the box?

**c.** What is the volume of the box?

**10.** Cement is sold by the cubic yard. A cubic yard of cement is the amount of cement that would fit into a box 1 yd long, 1 yd wide, and 1 yd high. How many cubic yards of cement are needed to make a rectangular patio 9 yards long, $6\frac{1}{2}$ yards wide and 6 inches ($\frac{1}{6}$ yard) thick?

**11.** Mali keeps her favorite amethyst in a cubic box with a volume of 343 cubic centimeters. What is the surface area of her box? Show your work.

**12.** The Tennis for Champs company is looking into new ways to package tennis balls. The packaging engineer at the company is exploring options for vacuum packing the balls (removing the air from the containers in which they are packaged) so they will retain good bounce. He wonders how much air there is in a standard container of tennis balls. Find the amount of empty space in a cylindrical container that is 18 centimeters tall and contains three tennis balls 6 centimeters in diameter.

**13.** Ms. Wohlshied has to purchase paper cups and containers of
water for the track-and-field competition. She knows that
students often use a cup only once and then throw it away. She
buys cone-shaped cups because they are nice for holding and
don't cost very much. This is an illustration of the cups she buys.

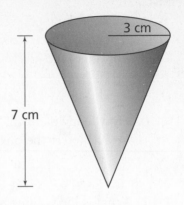

**a.** How many cubic centimeters of water does the cone-shaped
cup hold?

**b.** If Ms. Wohlshied buys water in 1-liter jugs, about how many empty
cups can be filled from one jug of water? (1 liter = 1,000 cubic centimeters)

**c.** How many times greater is the volume of a cone with a radius of
6 centimeters and a height of 7 centimeters than the volume of
Ms. Wohlshied's cup?

**d.** How many times greater is the volume of a cone with a radius of
3 centimeters and a height of 14 centimeters than the volume of
Ms. Wohlshied's cup?

**e.** How many times greater is the volume of a cone with a radius of
6 centimeters and a height of 14 centimeters than the volume of
Ms. Wohlshied's cup?

# Check-Up 1

1. Geoffrey is babysitting his little sister Sara and her two friends, Cela and Katie. Sara is wearing red, Cela is wearing blue and Katie is wearing green.

   Geoffrey fills a bucket with 12 red marbles, 8 blue marbles and 4 green marbles. He tells the girls that they will play a new game. He will reach into the bucket and pull out a marble at random. The girl whose clothes match the color of the marble scores 1 point.

   a. What is the probability of each girl scoring 1 point on the first draw?

   Sara:

   Cela:

   Katie:

   b. What is the probability of not drawing a green marble on the first draw?

   c. If two marbles of each color are added to the bucket, do the probabilities in part (a) change? Explain your reasoning.

   d. If the number of each color is doubled, do the probabilities in part (a) change? Explain why or why not.

# Check-Up 1 (continued)

**2.** Let's Make a Meal is a restaurant that lets customers design their own meals by choosing items from two categories: one entree and one drink for $2.99.

**a.** How many different meals can be designed?

### Kid's Choice Menu

| Entrees | Drinks |
|---------|--------|
| Hamburger | Milk |
| Hot dog | Soda |
| Pizza | |
| Chicken | |

**b.** If meals are made randomly, what is the probability that a meal will include a hamburger?

**c.** If meals are made randomly, what is the probability of a meal having a chicken and a soda?

**d.** For $0.99 more, you can also have a dessert: either apple pie or ice cream. How many different meals can be designed that include a dessert?

# Partner Quiz

1. Matt has three pairs of dark socks and six pairs of white socks in his sock drawer. Each pair is rolled together. He wants to use them to help choose his school clothes this morning.

First, he will close his eyes to select a pair of socks. If the socks are dark, Matt will choose an outfit that includes the dress pants that his mother bought. If the socks are white, Matt will toss a coin. If he gets heads, he will wear jeans. If he gets tails, he will wear shorts.

   **a.** What is the probability that Matt will wear white socks to school?

   **b.** What is the probability that Matt will wear shorts to school?

   **c.** What is the probability that Matt will wear dress pants to school?

   **d.** What is the probability that Matt will wear jeans with dark socks?

   **e.** Is Matt equally likely to wear dress pants, shorts, and jeans today? Explain your answer.

**Partner Quiz** *(continued)*

2. Maja was analyzing a Path game similar to those you worked on in this unit. In her game, the arrangement of paths and forks leads into Cave A, Cave B, or Cave C. Maja made an area model to analyze the probability of ending in each room.

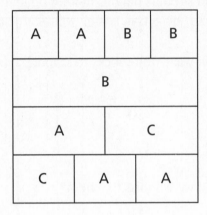

a. What is the probability of ending in Cave A? In Cave B? In Cave C?

b. Draw a picture of the paths and forks that could be represented by Maja's area model.

# Check-Up 2

Maribeth makes 70% of her free throws when she is in a two-try free-throw situation. Her coach notices that she gets nervous in a one-and-one free-throw situation and only makes 50% of those free throws.

**1.** Construct an area model for each of Maribeth's free-throw situations.

**Two-try Free-throw
Situation**

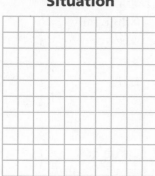

**One-and-one Free-throw
Situation**

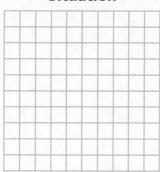

**2.** What is Maribeth's average number of points per situation for each type of free-throw situation?

**3.** Maribeth was fouled 50 times this season. Of these, 20 were two-try free-throw situations and 30 were one-and-one free-throw situations. How many points would you expect her to have scored for free throws this season?

# Multiple-Choice Items

1. Using the letters M, A, T, and H only once, how many 3-letter combinations are there (regardless of order)?

   **A.** 12          **B.** 8          **C.** 24          **D.** 32

2. On any given day, the cafeteria offers 3 main dishes for lunch (pizza, hamburger, or the featured item that day) and 3 kinds of drinks (white milk, chocolate milk, or apple juice). How many possible choices are there for lunch?

   **F.** 3          **G.** 6          **H.** 9          **J.** 12

3. Candice is the best hitter on her high school softball team. She gets on base safely 60% of the time. What is the probability that her next at bat will result in her getting on base?

   **A.** $\frac{3}{5}$          **B.** $\frac{1}{6}$          **C.** $\frac{1}{2}$          **D.** $\frac{2}{5}$

4. Justine decides to toss 2 coins 100 times. Which results should occur most often?

   **F.** Two heads                    **G.** Two tails

   **H.** One head, one tail           **J.** All of these combinations are equally likely

5. The probability of rolling a 6 on a regular number cube is $\frac{1}{6}$. If Jacob tosses a number cube 24 times, how many times would he expect to roll a 6?

   **A.** 2          **B.** 4          **C.** 3          **D.** 5

## Multiple-Choice Items (continued)

6. What is the probability of spinning a multiple of 4 on the spinner below?

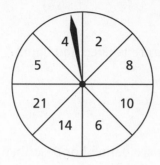

    **F.** $\frac{1}{2}$             **G.** $\frac{1}{4}$             **H.** $\frac{3}{4}$             **J.** $\frac{3}{8}$

7. J'Mesha and Aarti each bought a gift and wanted to have it wrapped at the store. The store offers 2 designs of paper (solid or polka dots) and each design comes in 3 different colors. If the clerk chooses the paper randomly, what is the probability that the gifts will get wrapped identically?

    **A.** $\frac{1}{2}$             **B.** $\frac{1}{3}$             **C.** $\frac{2}{6}$             **D.** $\frac{1}{6}$

# Notebook Checklist

**Place a ✓ next to each item you have completed.**

## Notebook Organization

_____ Problems and Mathematical Reflections are labeled and dated.

_____ Work is neat and easy to find and follow.

## Vocabulary

_____ All words are listed.      _____ All words are defined or described.

## Assessments

_____ Check-Up 1          _____ Check-Up 2

_____ Partner Quiz        _____ Unit Test

## Assignments

_____ _____     _____ _____

_____ _____     _____ _____

_____ _____     _____ _____

_____ _____     _____ _____

_____ _____     _____ _____

_____ _____     _____ _____

_____ _____     _____ _____

_____ _____     _____ _____

_____ _____     _____ _____

_____ _____     _____ _____

_____ _____     _____ _____

_____ _____     _____ _____

_____ _____     _____ _____

_____ _____     _____ _____

# Self Assessment

**Mathematical Ideas**

After studying the mathematics in *What Do You Expect?*:

**1. a.** I learned these things about probability and expected value:

**b.** Here are page numbers of notebook entries that give evidence of what I have learned, along with descriptions of what each entry shows:

**2. a.** The mathematical ideas that I am still struggling with:

**b.** This is why I think these ideas are difficult for me:

**c.** Here are page numbers of notebook entries that give evidence of what I am struggling with, along with descriptions of what each entry shows:

**Class Participation**

I contributed to the classroom **discussion** and understanding of *What Do You Expect?* when I . . . (Give examples.)

# Self Assessment (continued)

**Learning Environment**

**Rate the learning activities using this scale:**

**1** I consistently struggled to understand the mathematics and I'm still not sure that I know it.

**2** I struggled somewhat but now I understand more than I did.

**3** I had to work, but I feel confident that I understand now.

**4** I understood everything pretty easily and I feel confident that I know the mathematics in these problems.

**5** Everything came easily. I knew most of the mathematics before we did this.

**Learning Activities:**

_____ Problems from the Investigations

_____ ACE Homework Assignments

_____ Mathematical Reflections

_____ Check-Ups

_____ Partner Quiz

_____ Unit Test

**Check any of the following that you feel are the most helpful in adding to the success of your learning.**

❏ Working on my own in class.

❏ Discussing a problem with a partner.

❏ Working in a small group of 3 or 4 people.

❏ Discussing a problem as a whole class.

❏ Individual or group presentation to the whole class.

❏ Hearing how other people solved the problem.

❏ Summarizing the mathematics as a class and taking notes.

❏ Completing homework assignments.

# Unit Test

1. Three chips are tossed. The red chip has a side A and a side B. The yellow chip has a side B and a side C. The blue chip has both sides marked A.

   **a.** Which is greater: the probability of getting exactly 2 Bs or the probability of getting exactly 2 As? Explain your reasoning.

   **b.** What is the probability of not getting at least one B?

   **c.** What is the probability that none of the three sides match?

2. Two identical containers contain marbles. Container 1 has 2 white marbles and one red marble. Container 2 has one white marble and one red marble. Suppose you select a container at random and then draw out a marble. What is the probability of drawing a white marble?

3. Tua has created a new game called Making Green. To play the game, a player spins twice. If the player gets blue in one section and yellow in the other, the player wins, because blue and yellow together make green. The player can choose either spinner for either of their two spins.

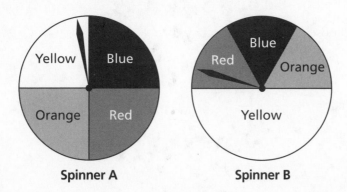

**Spinner A**     **Spinner B**

   **a.** Tua spins Spinner A once and Spinner B once. What is the probability she will get green? Explain.

   **b.** Is there a different choice of selecting the spinners to make the probability of making green greater than that in part (a)? Explain your reasoning.

# Unit Test (continued)

**4.** A family has exactly three children. What is the probability that they have

    **a.** a girl, a boy, and a girl in that order?

    **b.** exactly two boys?

    **c.** all girls?

**5.** You are offered the following choices for baby sitting:

$6 per job or the amount of money you get by drawing two bills from a bag containing one $10 bill and four $1 bills. (You do not replace the first bill you draw.)

    **a.** How much money could you expect to average per hour over the long run if you select to draw out of the bag each time you baby sit?

    **b.** Which plan would you choose?

# Question Bank

Assign these questions as additional homework, or use them as review, quiz, or test questions.

1. A bag contains two green marbles, four yellow marbles, six blue marbles, and eight red marbles. Draws of marbles are made randomly.

   a. What is the probability of drawing a blue marble?

   b. What is the probability of not drawing a blue marble?

   c. If you double the number of green, yellow, blue, and red marbles in the bag, what will be the probability of drawing a blue marble?

   d. How does your answer to part (c) compare with your answer to part (a)? Explain.

   e. If you add two of each color to the original bag of marbles, what will be the probability of drawing a blue marble?

   f. How does your answer to part (e) compare with your answer to part (a)? Explain.

   g. How many blue marbles would you need to add to the original bag of marbles to make the probability of drawing a blue marble $\frac{1}{2}$?

2. A bag contains two red marbles and two white marbles.

   a. After a marble is drawn, it is replaced before the next draw. What is the probability that a red marble will be drawn twice in a row? Explain.

   b. If a marble is drawn and is not replaced before the second marble is drawn, what is the probability that two red marbles will be drawn? Explain.

3. Brianna and Emmanuel are given another chance to win prizes on the Gee Whiz Everyone Wins! game show. Brianna arranges three red marbles and three green marbles in two containers while Emmanuel is out of the room. Emmanuel will choose a container and draw out one marble. If he draws a red marble, the friends each win a prize. What arrangement of marbles in the container will give the friends the best chance of winning?

**4.** Kim spun a spinner 100 times and made a record of her results.

| Outcome | Blue | Red |
|---|---|---|
| Number of times | 86 | 14 |

**a.** Which spinner below did Kim most likely use? Explain.

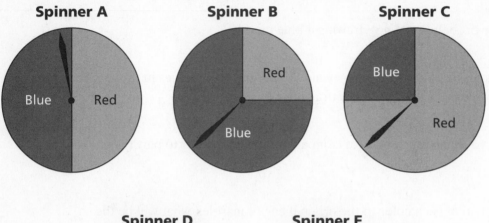

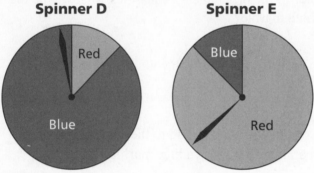

**b.** If Kim spins Spinner B twice, what is the probability that she will get blue on both spins?

**5.** Many states run a lottery in which a three-digit number is chosen at random each day. To win, a player must guess what three-digit number will be drawn.

**a.** If each of the three digits can be 0 through 9, how many different numbers can be chosen?

**b.** If someone buys one ticket, what is the probability of winning on any one draw?

**c.** If the payoff on a $1 bet is $750, what could a player expect to win over the long run?

**d.** Are lotteries like this one fair games of chance? Why might a state run a game that is not fair to the players?

6. Kenisha created a new screen for the path game.

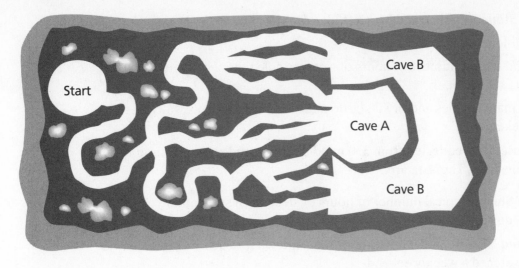

**a.** If Zark randomly selects a path at each fork, what is the theoretical probability that he will end in Cave A? End in Cave B?

**b.** If you played this game 72 times, how many times could you expect Zark to end in Cave A? End in Cave B?

# Check-Up

**Middle School Students' Sleep and Movie/Video Habits**

A group of middle school students wondered:

- What's the typical number of hours of sleep middle school students get during the school week?
- Just how many movies and/or videos do middle school students watch in a week/weekend?

This check-up uses data collected from 330 middle school students to be used to answer these questions. The data are:

> **Hours of Sleep** – typical number of hours of sleep each student had per night during a week
>
> **Movies and Videos** – the number of movies and videos each student watched a week/weekend

For each student, we also know:

> **Grade** – sixth, seventh, or eighth
>
> **Sex** – boy or girl

1. Describe how you think these data were collected.

## Check-Up (continued)

**2.** Here is a graph that shows the numbers of movies and videos watched during a week/weekend by each of the 330 students.

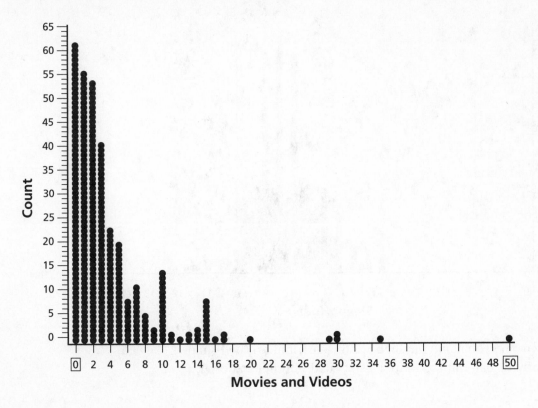

**a.** How would you name the shape of this distribution (bell-shaped, skewed, uniform or flat, clumped with clusters in different locations)?

**b.** Describe the variability in this distribution.

**c.** Draw and label a line that shows where you estimate the median would be located. Explain your reasoning.

**d.** Draw and label a line that shows where you estimate the mean would be located. Explain your reasoning.

**Check-Up** *(continued)*

**3.** Here is a graph that shows the typical hours of sleep per night during a week each of the 330 students had.

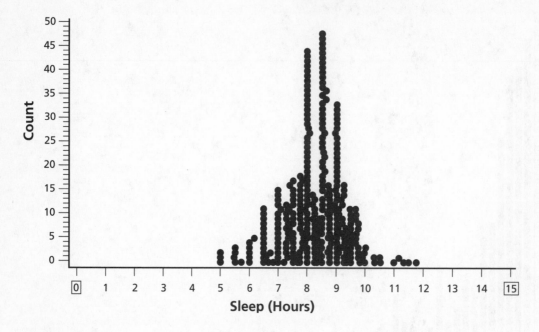

**a.** How would you name the shape of this distribution (bell-shaped, skewed, uniform or flat, clumped with clusters in different locations)?

**b.** Describe the variability in this distribution.

**c.** Draw and label a line that shows where you estimate the median would be located. Explain your reasoning.

**d.** Draw and label a line that shows where you estimate the mean would be located. Explain your reasoning.

# Partner Quiz

**Reaction Times**

1. Jeff looked at fastest trials for the 40 students when they used their dominant hands (DH) and when they used their non-dominant hands (NDH). Below are graphs that show the two distributions.

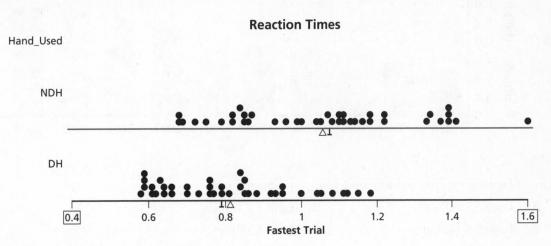

**Reaction Times**

Hand_Used

a. Estimate these statistics from looking at the graphs.

Mean reaction time with DH:          Mean reaction time with NDH:

Median reaction time with DH:        Median reaction time with NDH:

Range of reaction times for DH:      Range of reaction times for NDH:

b. Jeff wondered, "How much faster are students when they use their dominant hands (DH) than when they use their non-dominant hands (NDH)?" Write a response to Jeff's question. Explain your reasoning. You can use the statistics you estimated in part (a) and also talk about where data cluster, where there are gaps, and if there are any outliers.

# Multiple-Choice Items

Use the following graph to answer Exercises 1 – 2:

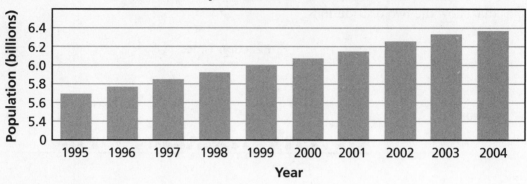

**Mid-Year Population for the World 1995–2004**

1. In 1995, what was the world's mid-year population?

   **A.** about 5.7 billion

   **B.** about 5.8 billion

   **C.** about 5.9 billion

   **D.** about 6 billion

2. Which statement describes the change in the world's mid-year population from 1995 to 2004?

   **F.** decreases by approximately 25%

   **G.** decreases by approximately 10%

   **H.** increases by approximately 25%

   **J.** increases by approximately 10%

## Multiple-Choice Items (continued)

Use the following graph to answer Exercises 3 – 4:

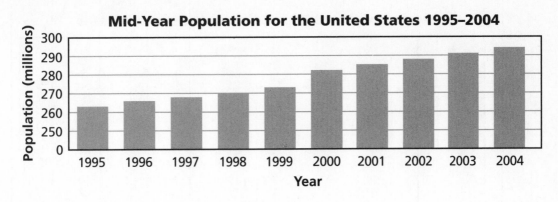

**Mid-Year Population for the United States 1995–2004**

3. In 1995, what was the mid-year population of the United States?

   A. about 260 million

   B. about 263 million

   C. about 268 million

   D. about 270 million

4. Which statement describes the change in the mid-year population of the United States from 1995 to 2004?

   F. decreases by approximately 25%

   G. decreases by approximately 10%

   H. increases by approximately 25%

   J. increases by approximately 10%

# Multiple-Choice Items (continued)

**Use the following graphs to answer Exercises 5 – 6:**

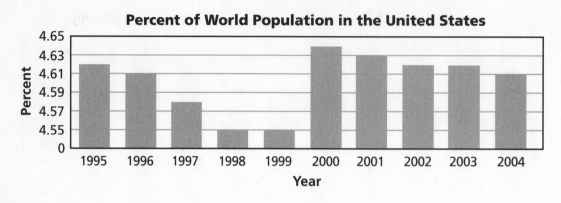

**Percent of World Population in the United States**

**5.** What percent of the 1995 world population is in the United States?

   **A.** about 4%

   **B.** about 4.6%

   **C.** about 40%

   **D.** about 46%

**6.** Which statement describes the trend in the percent of the world population that is in the United States?

   **F.** The percent of the world population that is in the United States has decreased greatly from 1995 to 2004.

   **G.** The percent of the world population that is in the United States has decreased slightly from 1995 to 2004.

   **H.** The percent of the world population that is in the United States stayed about the same from 1995 to 2004.

   **J.** The percent of the world population that is in the United States has increased slightly from 1995 to 2004.

**7.** Marcos wants an average of 90 or better in mathematics. His four test grades are 85, 88, 92, and 90. What is the lowest grade he can get on his next exam and still achieve his desired average?

   **A.** 84        **B.** 86        **C.** 90        **D.** 95

# Multiple-Choice Items (continued)

8. How does increasing the smaller values in a set of data affect the mean?

    F. The mean remains the same.

    G. The mean increases.

    H. The mean decreases.

    J. You cannot determine how the mean changes.

9. What percent of Roland's test scores are 86 or greater?

**Roland's Test Scores**

```
8 | 2 5 5 5 6 6 6 6 9 9 9 9
9 | 0 2 2 2
Key: 8 | 6 means 86
```

    A. 12%          B. 25%          C. 75%          D. 86%

10. Use the table below to determine which comparison statement is true.

**Locations of Wood and Steel Roller Coasters**

| Continent | Wood | Steel |
|---|---|---|
| Africa | 0 | 22 |
| Asia | 8 | 398 |
| Australia | 4 | 19 |
| Europe | 32 | 523 |
| North America | 129 | 605 |
| South America | 1 | 56 |
| Total | 174 | 1,623 |

    F. In Africa, there are 22 more wood roller coasters than steel coasters.

    G. Australia has about 4% of the wood roller coasters and 19% of the steel coasters.

    H. In North America, there are about double the number of wood roller coasters than steel coasters.

    J. About 25% of all the steel roller coasters are in Asia.

# Multiple-Choice Items (continued)

11. The local newspaper surveyed Morganville citizens for their opinions on whether to build a new highway. Compare the distributions of those who voted *for* building a new highway with those who voted *against* building a new highway. Which statement is true?

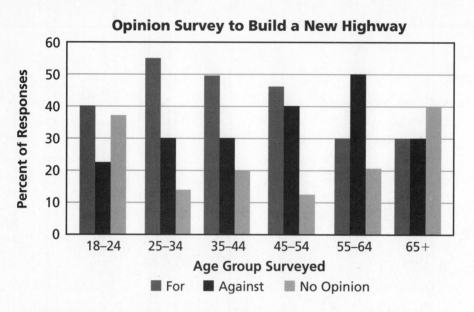

**Opinion Survey to Build a New Highway**

**A.** More of Morganville's younger citizens support a new highway than oppose it.

**B.** More of Morganville's younger citizens voted against building a new highway than for it.

**C.** The majority of both oldest and youngest respondents voted for building the highway.

**D.** Respondents from age 25 to age 64 were most likely to have no opinion.

# Notebook Checklist

**Place a ✓ next to each item you have completed.**

## Notebook Organization

_____ Problems and Mathematical Reflections are labeled and dated.

_____ Work is neat and easy to find and follow.

## Vocabulary

_____ All words are listed.     _____ All words are defined or described.

## Assessments

_____ Check-Up

_____ Partner Quiz

_____ Unit Test

## Assignments

_____ _____     _____ _____

_____ _____     _____ _____

_____ _____     _____ _____

_____ _____     _____ _____

_____ _____     _____ _____

_____ _____     _____ _____

_____ _____     _____ _____

_____ _____     _____ _____

_____ _____     _____ _____

_____ _____     _____ _____

_____ _____     _____ _____

_____ _____     _____ _____

_____ _____     _____ _____

_____ _____     _____ _____

_____ _____     _____ _____

# Self Assessment

## Mathematical Ideas

After studying the mathematics in *Data Distributions:*

**1. a.** I learned these things about describing variability and comparing groups:

    **b.** Here are page numbers of notebook entries that give evidence of what I have learned, along with descriptions of what each entry shows:

**2. a.** The mathematical ideas that I am still struggling with:

    **b.** This is why I think these ideas are difficult for me:

    **c.** Here are page numbers of notebook entries that give evidence of what I am struggling with, along with descriptions of what each entry shows:

## Class Participation

I contributed to the classroom **discussion** and understanding of *Data Distributions* when I . . . (Give examples.)

# Self Assessment (continued)

**Learning Environment**

**Rate the learning activities using this scale:**

**1** I consistently struggled to understand the mathematics and I'm still not sure that I know it.

**2** I struggled somewhat but now I understand more than I did.

**3** I had to work, but I feel confident that I understand now.

**4** I understood everything pretty easily and I feel confident that I know the mathematics in these problems.

**5** Everything came easily. I knew most of the mathematics before we did this.

**Learning Activities:**

_____ Problems from the Investigations

_____ ACE Homework Assignments

_____ Mathematical Reflections

_____ Check-Up

_____ Partner Quiz

_____ Unit Test

**Check any of the following that you feel are the most helpful in adding to the success of your learning.**

❏ Working on my own in class.

❏ Discussing a problem with a partner.

❏ Working in a small group of 3 or 4 people.

❏ Discussing a problem as a whole class.

❏ Individual or group presentation to the whole class.

❏ Hearing how other people solved the problem.

❏ Summarizing the mathematics as a class and taking notes.

❏ Completing homework assignments.

# Unit Test 1

## Part I

The PTA at Snow Camp Middle School is concerned that more and more teenagers are reporting back problems. Doctors think that many of these problems may be related to carrying backpacks that are too heavy. The PTA decides to put on an assembly to educate students in the school about the problem. The PTA also wants to know if the assembly succeeds in getting students to carry less in their backpacks.

One team of middle school students in Mrs. James's class decided to weigh students' backpacks both before and after the assembly. A week before the assembly, they randomly selected 79 students walking in the halls before school. The students took off their backpacks so the backpacks could be weighed on a scale. The weight of each backpack was recorded to the nearest half pound.

A month later, after the assembly, the team of students weighed another sample of students' backpacks using the same method—stopping students in the halls before school. The first period bell surprised them; they were only able to weigh the backpacks of 51 students.

Here is a graph showing the results.

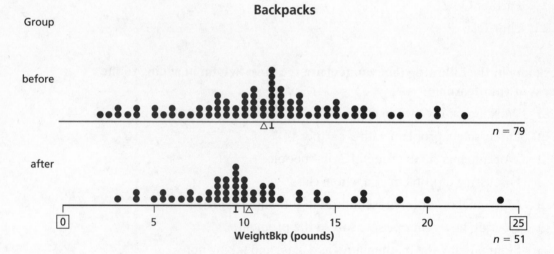

# Unit Test 1 *(continued)*

**1.** The PTA President wants to know what the results show about how much backpacks weighed before the assembly. Briefly summarize the data for her.

**2.** The PTA President also wants to know if the students are carrying less or more in their backpacks since the assembly. If so, how much less or more are they carrying than before the assembly?

**3.** Based on the data, was the assembly effective in influencing students to carry less weight in their backpacks? Explain why or why not.

# Unit Test 1 (continued)

## Part II

Here are some comments from members of the PTA. For each comment, say whether you agree or not and explain why.

1. Mr. Manley said, "I don't think you can decide anything from this study. Both before and after the study, there were students who carried a lot of weight and students who carried very little weight. So you really don't know anything about how much a student carried either before or after the assembly."

   Do you agree or disagree? Explain why.

2. Mrs. James said, "I think students after the assembly tend to carry less weight than students before the assembly carried, about 2 pounds less on average. If you look at the medians you'll see that the median weight for a backpack before the assembly is 11.5 pounds compared to a median of 9.5 after the assembly.

   Do you agree or disagree? Explain why.

Name _____ Date _____ Class _____

# Unit Test 2 Using Tinkerplots Software
·································································································
**Data Distributions**

**To be done using file:** BackpackDecision.tpl

**Part I – Complete and turn in to get Part II**

The PTA at Snow Camp Middle School is concerned that more and more
teenagers are reporting back problems. Doctors think that many of these
problems may be related to carrying backpacks that are too heavy. The PTA
decides to put on an assembly to educate students in the school about the
problem. The PTA also wants to know if the assembly succeeds in getting
students to carry less in their backpacks.

You and your partner have been asked to investigate this question.

What data would you collect? How would you go about determining whether
backpacks students carried weighed less after the assembly?

Once you've collected the data, what would you do with the data in order to
figure out whether the assembly made a difference?

# Unit Test 2 *(continued)*

**Part II – Complete and show your teacher both the graph and your written responses to get Part III.**

One team of middle school students decided to weigh students' backpacks both before and after the assembly. A week before the assembly, they randomly selected 79 students walking in the halls before school. The students took off their backpacks so the backpacks could be weighed on a scale. The weight of each backpack was recorded to the nearest half pound.

A month later, after the assembly, the team of students weighed another sample of students' backpacks using the same method—stopping students in the halls before school. The first period bell surprised them; they were only able to weigh the backpacks of 51 students.

**Open the file:** BackpackDecision.tpl

1. Look through the case cards for these data. What are the attributes? What kinds of data are found with each attribute?

2. Make one or more graphs to help you answer the questions below. You can write your answer to the questions in a text box on the computer and print out both your answers and graph(s) you made.

   a. The PTA President wants to know what the results show about how much backpacks weighed before the assembly. Briefly summarize the data for her.

   b. The PTA President also wants to know if the students are carrying less or more in their backpacks since the assembly. If so, how much less or more are they carrying than before the assembly?

   c. Based on the data, was the assembly effective in influencing students to carry less weight in their backpacks? Explain why or why not.

# Unit Test 2 (continued)

## Part III

Here are some comments from members of the PTA. For each comment, say whether you agree or not and explain why.

**1.** Mr. Manley said, "I don't think you can decide anything from this study. Both before and after the study, there were students who carried a lot of weight and students who carried very little weight. So you really don't know anything about how much a student carried either before or after the assembly."

Do you agree or disagree? Explain why.

**2.** Mrs. James said, "I think students after the assembly tend to carry less weight than students before the assembly carried, about 2 pounds less on average. If you look at the medians you'll see that the median weight for a backpack before the assembly is 11.5 pounds compared to a median of 9.5 after the assembly.

Do you agree or disagree? Explain why.

# Question Bank

**Use situations a – c below to answer Exercises 1–2.**

1. Are the data that are collected categorical or numerical?

2. For the situation, are the data likely to show a lot or a little variability? Explain your reasoning.

   **a.** Each carpenter's helper measures and records the length of the same wooden plank in centimeters.

   **b.** Each student records the number of pets to answer the question: What is the typical number of pets for students in the class?

   **c.** Each student records the time spent playing video games in the last week to answer the question: "How much variability is there in the times spent playing video games?"

3. Javier's test scores were 85, 85, 97, 98 and 100. His teacher told the class that they could choose which measure of center they wanted her to use to determine final grades. Which measure do you suggest that Javier choose?

   **A.** Mean          **B.** Median          **C.** Mode          **D.** Range

4. Six days' temperatures in April have an average that is 12 degrees higher than six days' temperatures in March. What is the difference between the sums of the temperatures?

5. Use the medians, means, and ranges given below. Compare the number of movies watched by boys with the number of movies watched by girls during the summer. Explain your reasoning.

| Statistic | Number of Movies Watched by Boys During the Summer | Number of Movies Watched by Girls During the Summer |
|---|---|---|
| Mean | ≈5.3 | ≈5.07 |
| Median | 4 | 3 |
| Range | 17 | 14 |

# Question Bank (continued)

**6.** Below are two dot plots that display data about the number of hours boys slept and the number of hours girls slept on a Friday night. Means and medians are marked on each graph.

### Number of Hours Slept on Friday Night (boys)

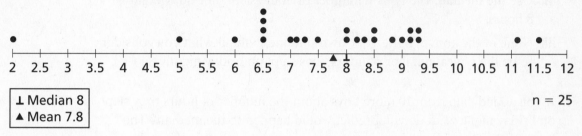

⊥ Median 8
▲ Mean 7.8

n = 25

### Number of Hours Slept on Friday Night (girls)

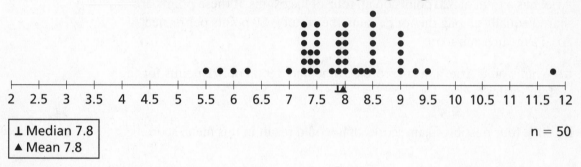

⊥ Median 7.8
▲ Mean 7.8

n = 50

**a.** Write two comparison statements comparing the number of hours the boys slept to the number of hours the girls slept.

**b.** What fraction of boys slept longer than the mean? What percent of boys slept longer than the mean?

**c.** What fraction of girls slept longer than the mean? What percent of girls slept longer than the mean?

**d.** The number of boys reporting sleep times is not the same as the number of girls reporting sleep times. If you made a frequency bar graph of each set of data, would you show the frequencies as counts or percents? Explain your reasoning.

    **e.** What is the typical number of hours slept for the boys on Friday night? Which statement seems to be a sensible answer? Explain your reasoning.

      **i.** Use the mode: The typical number of hours slept on Friday night is 6.5 hours.

     **ii.** Use the median: The typical number of hours slept on Friday night is 8 hours.

    **iii.** None of the above: Write your own statement about what you consider to be the typical number of hours boys slept on Friday night.

    **f.** If you added data from 10 more boys about the number of hours they slept on Friday night, what do you predict would happen to the median? The mean? The range? Explain your reasoning.

**7.** Ariel has a total of 320 points on all four of his exams. If these points are shared equally among the four exams, the result is 80 points per project—Ariel's mean exam score.

    **a.** What would Ariel's mean score be if he had a total of 372 points for the four exams?

    **b.** Give four possible exam scores that would result in this mean score.

    **c.** What is the range of the scores for these four exam scores? What does this tell you about the variability of the scores?

8. Five good friends have the following numbers of basketball cards:

   Glen: 352      Benny: 347      Yari: 265      Jillian: 261      Mark: 325

   a. What is the range of number of cards of the five friends? What does the range tell you about the variability in the amount of cards they have?

   b. The five friends decided to share their cards equally. How many cards per friend will this be? Explain your reasoning.

   c. The five friends forgot about another friend, Susanna, when cards were shared. Susanna has 261 cards, the same number of cards as Jillian. If Susanna's cards are included with the others' cards and shared equally among the six friends, will the first five friends now receive less, the same as, or more than they did before Susanna's cards were included? Explain.

9. Another group of five friends shared their basketball cards equally. The result was 364 cards per friend. Does this mean that one of the friends originally received 364 basketball cards? Explain.

10. Four friends wanted to share their costs for lunch equally among themselves. Their meals cost $4.50, $3.50, $4.20, $3.50. Mandy said that because two of the meals cost the same you needed to only divide the total cost of the meals by 3. Enrico disagreed and said that no matter whether the meals cost the same amount, you would still divide them equally among the 4 friends. Do you agree with Mandy or Enrico? Explain.

11. John's baseball team made the following number of runs for their first 15 games: 0, 0, 0, 1, 1, 1, 1, 2, 2, 2, 3, 3, 4, 5, 8. To figure out the team's average runs per game, John said not to include the 0 runs because they did not increase the amount of their total runs. Do you agree with John's reasoning? Explain.

12. The following data are the number of hours of homework done by several students on a Monday night: 0.5, 0.5, 1, 1, 1, 1, 2, 3. If you replaced data from a student who did 0.5 hour of homework with one who did 2 hours of homework:

   a. Does the mean change? If so, how does it change and why?

   b. Does the median change? If so, how does it change and why?

   c. Does the range change? If so, how does it change and why?

**13.** Below are data from two bags of Crispy M&M's® candies that were opened.

| Bag | Green | Yellow | Orange | Blue | Brown | Red | Total |
|---|---|---|---|---|---|---|---|
| 1 | 8 | 10 | 8 | 10 | 9 | 9 | 54 |
| 2 | 8 | 9 | 7 | 10 | 10 | 11 | 55 |

**a.** Find the percent of each color for bags 1 and 2.

**b.** Make a bar graph for each set of data that shows the percent of each color found in that bag of candies.

**c.** For each graph, write two or more sentences describing the data displayed on the graph.

**d.** Are there any similarities or differences in the patterns between the two bags of Crispy M&M's candies that can be used to answer the question, "Is there some plan to the distribution of colors of Crispy M&M's candies in a bag?" Explain your reasoning.

**e.** Below are data from thirty bags of Crispy M&M's candies that were opened. Make a bar graph for these data that shows the percent of each color found in the thirty bags of candies.

| Bag | Green | Yellow | Orange | Blue | Brown | Red | Total |
|---|---|---|---|---|---|---|---|
| 1–30 | 250 | 285 | 260 | 275 | 280 | 280 | 1,630 |

**f.** Write two or more sentences describing the data displayed by the graph.

**g.** How would you now answer the original question, "Is there some plan to the distribution of colors of Crispy M&M's candies in a bag?

**14.** At the right is a copy of the distribution of the number of pets for Marie and her friends. The location of the mean is at 2.71 pets and the median is at 3 pets.

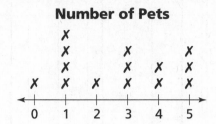

**Number of Pets**

   a. What happens to the mean and the median if a friend with 3 pets is removed and her data is replaced with data from three new friends, each of whom has 1 pet? Why do you think this happens?

   b. What happens to the mean and the median in the original distribution if you remove a friend with 1 pet and replace her with a friend who has 4 pets? Why do you think this happens?

**Use the following bar graphs to answer Exercises 15 and 16.**

**15.** Compare the variability in heights in the following distributions. Be sure to discuss clusters and ranges in your comparisons.

**16.** Where do you predict the mean and median will be in each distribution? Explain your reasoning.

**County Youth Girls Gymnasts' Heights**

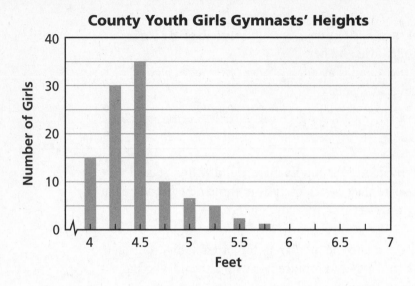

**County Youth Boys Basketball Players' Heights**

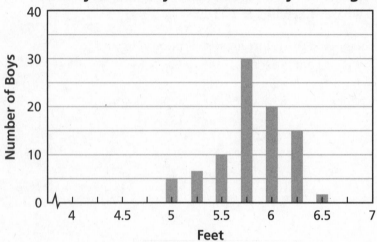

**County "Guardian & Child Dance" Attendees' Heights**

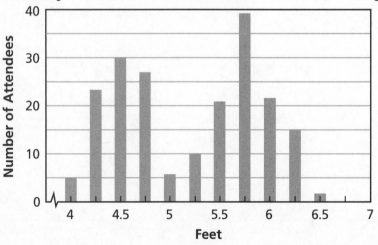

# Variables and Patterns Assessment Answers

## Check-Up 1

1. **a.** Number of seconds; total knee bends
   **b.** **Deep Knee Bends**

| Time (seconds) | Knee Bends |
|---|---|
| 10 | 10 |
| 20 | 18 |
| 30 | 27 |
| 40 | 36 |
| 50 | 45 |
| 60 | 53 |
| 70 | 58 |
| 80 | 62 |
| 90 | 65 |
| 100 | 68 |
| 110 | 70 |
| 120 | 72 |

   **c.** Stefan begins by doing approximately nine knee bends every ten seconds, but as time goes on the number of knee bends really decreases down to about two knee bends for every ten seconds.
   **d.** In 25 seconds, he should have done about 22 or 23 knee bends.
   In 65 seconds, he should have done about 55 or 56 knee bends.
2. **a.** Time and Distance
   **b.** **Anita's Walk**

   **c.** She made the most progress at the beginning walking 1 mile in the first 10 minutes. (A student may say 0 to 5 minutes or 5 to 10 minutes.)
   On the table, this shows up as the largest increase from one distance to the next. On the graph, this shows up as the steepest line segment connecting the points.
   **d.** Anita made the least progress from 25 minutes to 30 minutes walking only 0.05 of a mile.
   On the table, this shows up as the smallest increase from one distance to the next. On the graph, this shows up as the least steep line segment connecting the points.

## Check-Up 2

1. **a.** **Earnings**

| Time (hours) | Money |
|---|---|
| 1 | $4.50 |
| 2 | $9.00 |
| 3 | $13.50 |
| 4 | $18.00 |
| 5 | $22.50 |
| 6 | $27.00 |
| 7 | $31.50 |
| 8 | $36.00 |

# Variables and Patterns Assessment Answers (continued)

**b.**

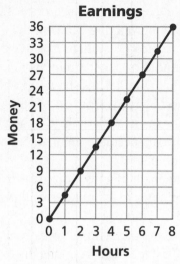

**Earnings**

c. Students may argue for or against connecting the dots. When people work part of an hour they are often paid for the full hour, in which case it would not be continuous.

d. About 4.5 hours

e. $24.75

2. a. As time passes, speed increases at a steady rate.

b. As time passes, speed decreases at a steady rate.

c. The person goes at an accelerating pace for a short time, then continues on still accelerating, but not so rapidly.

3. a. Days of collecting, Number of cans collected

b. Day 1, about 78 cans

c. Day 1 → 78, Day 2 → 60, Day 3 → 60, Day 4 → 34, Day 5 → 63
Total is about 295 cans

d. No, it does not make sense to connect the points (unless you just want to see the pattern). You could not have collected partial cans.

## Partner Quiz

1. a. **Dominic's and Norm's Savings**

| Weeks | Dominic's Money | Norm's Money |
|---|---|---|
| 0 | 0 | 25 |
| 1 | 10 | 32 |
| 2 | 20 | 39 |
| 3 | 30 | 46 |
| 4 | 40 | 53 |
| 5 | 50 | 60 |
| 6 | 60 | 67 |
| 7 | 70 | 74 |
| 8 | 80 | 81 |
| 9 | 90 | 88 |
| 10 | 100 | 95 |

b. From the directions students may write the rule in words or symbols. (Students will be more likely to give a rule in words since they have not written symbolic rules with a constant while working this unit.)
Dominic: Number of weeks times 10 equals total saved
$$10w = s$$
Norm: Number of weeks times 7 plus 25 equals the total saved.
$$7w + 25 = s$$

c. **Dominic's and Norm's Savings**

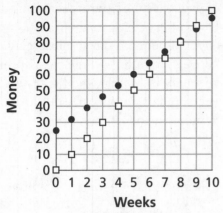

**Weeks**

-□- Dominic  -●- Norm

**Walk to the Movies**

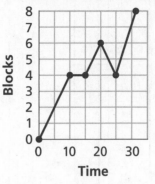

**Time**

d. No, not if they put their money in at the end of the week. At 8 weeks they will be very close. Dominic will have $80 and Norm will have $81. If they save parts of the amounts during the week, they could have the same amount between the 8th and 9th weeks.

e. Dominic will have enough money in 19 weeks.
Norm will have enough in 24 weeks.

## Multiple-Choice Items

1. A
2. H
3. C
4. F
5. B
6. G
7. B
8. J
9. C

## 2. Walk to the Movies

| Time | Blocks |
|------|--------|
| 0 | 0 |
| 10 | 4 |
| 15 | 4 |
| 20 | 6 |
| 25 | 4 |
| 31 | 8 |

OR

## Walk to the Movies

| Time | Blocks |
|------|--------|
| 4:25 | 0 |
| 4:35 | 4 |
| 4:40 | 4 |
| 4:45 | 6 |
| 4:50 | 4 |
| 4:56 | 8 |

# Variables and Patterns Assessment Answers *(continued)*

## Unit Test

**1. a.** Possible answer:

**Cost of Shirts**

| Number of Shirts | Cost |
|---|---|
| 1 | $6.95 |
| 2 | $13.90 |
| 3 | $20.85 |
| 4 | $27.80 |
| 5 | $34.75 |
| 6 | $41.70 |
| 7 | $48.65 |

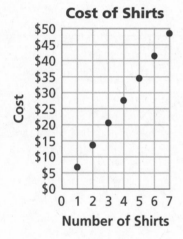

**Cost of Shirts**

**b.** Answers will vary. The points should not be connected because you cannot purchase a portion of a shirt. However, some students may make the point that the cost grows steadily so you could connect the points to see the pattern. $6.95s = c$, where $s$ is the number of shirts and $c$ is the cost of the shirts

**2.** Possible answer: Sam was paid a lot each day for babysitting his visiting aunt's children. Then the aunt left and steadily, over time, he spent almost all of his money.

**3.** In January, the number of daylight hours is only about 10. Through the months from January to June the number of daylight hours increases. Then in July the number of daylight hours starts decreasing and by December is back to about 10 hours of daylight per day. The greatest increase between months is in the early spring, February to March. And the faster decrease is in in the early fall, around September to October.

**4. a.**

**Cost of CDs**

| Number of CDs | Taylor's Department Store | Buyer's Warehouse |
|---|---|---|
| 01 | $15.49 | $37 |
| 02 | $30.98 | $49 |
| 03 | $46.47 | $61 |
| 04 | $61.96 | $73 |
| 05 | $77.45 | $85 |
| 06 | $92.94 | $97 |
| 07 | $108.43 | $109 |
| 08 | $123.92 | $121 |
| 09 | $139.41 | $133 |
| 10 | $154.90 | $145 |

**b.** $\text{Cost}_{\text{Taylor's}} = \$15.49n$
$\text{Cost}_{\text{Buyer's}} = \$25 + 12n$

**c.** 8 CDs or more

**d.** Fewer than 8 CDs. Students should refer to the table (or a graph) to show that for up to 7 CDs, Taylor's is cheaper.

**5. a.**

**Dots in Figures**

| Figure | 1 | 2 | 3 | 4 | 5 | 6 | 7 | 8 | 9 | 10 |
|---|---|---|---|---|---|---|---|---|---|---|
| Number of Dots | 3 | 6 | 9 | 12 | 15 | 18 | 21 | 24 | 27 | 30 |

**b.** $d$ represents the number of dots needed
$n$ represents the Figure number
$$d = 3n$$

# Variables and Patterns Assessment Answers (continued)

## Question Bank

**1. a.** The two variables are the number of breaths and the number of meters swum.

**b.**

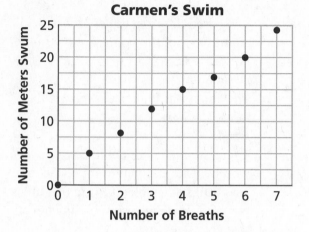

Carmen's Swim

**c.** Answers will vary. Students may argue for or against connecting the points. Some may say that breathing is continuous, but in swimming the breaths are more defined.

**d.** Carmen made the most progress during the first breath.

   **i.** In the table the distance increases from 0 to 5 meters for the first breath. This is the largest between any two breaths.

   **ii.** The part of the graph between the origin and the corresponding point, $(0, 5)$ is the steepest on the graph.

**e.** The least progress is a change of 2 meters, which occurs between breaths 4 and 5.

   **i.** In the table, this is the smallest distance between any two breaths.

   **ii.** The section of the graph between corresponding points on the graph $(4, 15)$ and $(5, 17)$ is the least steep section on the graph.

**f.** About 14 or 15 breaths

**2. a.** Elizabeth makes the most progress at two different times—in the first 25 minutes and from 40 to 45 minutes. This progress is shown on the graph by the steepest inclines.

**b.** She makes the least progress from 25 to 40 minutes. This is shown by the flattest incline.

**3. a.** The figures shown are regular polygons; however, students do not have to draw regular polygons to answer the questions. (Figure 2)

**b.** $d = n - 3$

**c.** (Figure 2)

**d.** $r = n - 2$

**e. i.** 18    **ii.** 48    **iii.** 998    **iv.** 999,998

**Figure 2**

### Polygons

| Sides | 4 | 5 | 6 | 7 | 8 | 9 | 10 |
|---|---|---|---|---|---|---|---|
| Diagonals | 1 | 2 | 3 | 4 | 5 | 6 | 7 |
| Regions | 2 | 3 | 5 | 5 | 6 | 7 | 8 |

# Variables and Patterns Assessment Answers *(continued)*

4. **a.** About 380 cartons
   **b.** About 50 cartons
   **c.** Between 11:30 and 11:45 and between 12:45 and 1:00
   **d.** Between noon and 12:15, between 12:30 and 12:45, and between 1:15 and 1:30
   **e.** The number of milk cartons available during the day decreased rapidly with breaks at noon, 12:30, and 1:15.
   **f.** Answers may vary. Possible answer: The points should not be connected because they cannot sell part of a milk carton.
   **g.** Answers will vary. Some students might say no because the graph gives a picture of what happened. Others might say yes because it would be helpful to have more specific information, especially since the $y$-axis has a fairly large scale.

5. Answers will vary. Possible answer: $y$ is the distance a bicyclist covers at an average speed of 8 miles per hour.

Y is the cost for tickets to a concert that cost $8 each.
Y is the cost for babysitting that cost $8 an hour

6. **a.** Yes, they both graphed the same data. They used different scales. But the coordinates of the points are the same. For example, $(0, 0)$, $(1, 80)$ . . . $(2.5, 200)$ lie on both graphs.
   **b.** The equations for each graph are the same: $y = 80x$.

7. **a.** $y = 4x$
   **b.** There are many possibilities:
   $y$ is the distance in miles for a walker who walks at an average rate of 4 miles per hour. Y is the cost of buying tickets that cost $4 each.
   In a certain game a player receives 4 points for each win. $y$ is the number of points a player wins after $x$ wins.

# Stretching and Shrinking Assessment Answers

## Check-Up 1

1. a. 12 cm by 15 cm
   b. 25%     c. $\frac{1}{4}$
   d. The corresponding angles in both photos will have the same measures.
   e. Perimeter of original = 36 cm
      Perimeter of reduced = 9 cm
      The perimeter of the original is 4 times the size of the reduced photo. OR
      The perimeter of the reduced photo will be $\frac{1}{4}$ the perimeter of the original photo.
   f. Area of original = 80 cm$^2$.
      Area of reduced = 5 cm$^2$.
      The area of the original photo is 16 times as large as the area of the reduced photo. OR
      The area of the reduced photo will be $\frac{1}{16}$ the area of the original photo.

## Check-Up 2

1. a. Area = 12 square units
      Perimeter ≈ 16 units

   b.
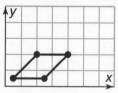

   | Point | (0.5x, 0.5y) |
   |-------|--------------|
   | E | (0.5, 0.5) |
   | F | (2, 2) |
   | G | (4, 2) |
   | H | (2.5, 0.5) |

### Parallelogram *EFGH*

   c. Area = 3 square units
      Perimeter ≈ 8 units
   d. (Figure 1)
   e. Area = 36 square units
      Perimeter ≈ 31 units
   f. *EFGH* is similar to *ABCD*, because the corresponding sides are related by the same scale factor, $\frac{1}{2}$. Also, corresponding angles appear to be equal.

2. Rectangle 1 is similar to Rectangle 2. The ratio of length to width is 3 to 2. Corresponding sides in Rectangles 1 and 2 are related by a scale factor of 1.5. The corresponding angles in Rectangles 1 and 2 have the same measure (all 90°).

3. a. side AC = 20, side AB = 16
   b. 4
   c. $\frac{1}{4}$
   d. The perimeter of ABC is 4 times the perimeter of triangle DEF.
   e. The area of triangle ABC is 16 times the area of triangle DEF.

4. a. side TR = 10 units
   b. side XZ = 26 units
   c. angle T = 110°
   d. angle Z = 20°

**Figure 1**

### Parallelogram JKLM

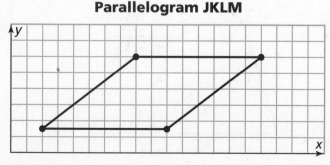

| Point | (2x, 1.5y) |
|-------|-----------|
| J | (2, 1.5) |
| K | (8, 6) |
| L | (16, 6) |
| M | (10, 1.5) |

# Stretching and Shrinking Assessment Answers *(continued)*

## Partner Quiz

1. **a.** (Figure 2)

   **b.** Ryan's and Simone's characters are similar: the shapes are the same, corresponding angles are the same measure, and the corresponding sides grow by the same scale factor. The scale factor from Ryan's character to Simone's character is 6.
   (Note: If students use the transitive property to answer this question—since Ryan's character is similar to Ashley's, and Ashley's is similar to Simone's, then Ryan's is similar to Simone's—you may want to ask them to support the answer with an explanation based on the properties of similar figures.)

   **c.** $(6x, 6y)$

2. **a.** Any rule in which the coefficient of $x$ is relatively large compared to the coefficient of $y$ will work; for example, $(5x, 2y)$ or $(3x, y)$ or $(10x, 0.5y)$

   **b.** Student should add some positive number to the second coordinate in their rule from part a; for example, $(5x, 2y + 4)$ or $(3x, y + 3)$ or $(10x, 0.5y + 8)$

   **c.** Slug is not similar to Mug, because Slug is stretched more horizontally than vertically. The figures have different shapes, different angles, and no consistent scale factor.

3. Shapes A and B are similar. They have the same basic shape, corresponding angles are equal, and the side lengths of shape A are about 3 times the corresponding side lengths of B. (Note: Students may determine this by measuring, tracing, or cutting out the two shapes to compare their angles and sides.)

## Multiple Choice Items

**1.** B    **2.** F    **3.** C    **4.** F

**Figure 2**

**Ryan's One-eyed Character**

**Simone's One-eyed Character**

# Stretching and Shrinking Assessment Answers (continued)

## Unit Test

**1.** 2

**2.** H since the scale factor is 2.
(The perimeter of the enlarged figure is 12 units. The perimeter of the original is 6 units. So, $12 \div 6 = 2$.)

**3.** D since the scale factor is 2.
(The area of the enlarged figure is 8 square units. The area of the original is 2 square units. So, $8 \div 2 = 4$.)

**4.** 200%

**5.** $\frac{1}{2}$

**6.** F since the scale factor is $\frac{1}{2}$.

(The perimeter of the reduced figure is 3 units. The perimeter of the original is 6 units. So $3 \div 6 = 0.5$.)

**7.** C since the scale factor is $\frac{1}{2}$.

(The area of the reduced figure is 0.5 square units. The area of the original is 2 square units. So, $0.5 \div 2 = 0.25$.)

**8.** 50%

**9. a.**

### Wump Backpacks

| Backpack 1 | Backpack 2 | Backpack 3 | Backpack 4 |
|---|---|---|---|
| $(x, y)$ | $(2x, 2y)$ | $(x + 8, y - 2)$ | $(x, 2y)$ |
| (0, 2) | (0, 4) | (8, 0) | (0, 4) |
| (8, 2) | (16, 4) | (16, 0) | (8, 4) |
| (6, 5) | (12, 10) | (14, 3) | (6, 10) |
| (2, 5) | (4, 10) | (10, 3) | (2, 10) |
| (0, 2) | (0, 4) | (8, 0) | (0, 4) |

**b.**

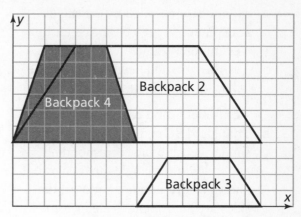

**c.** Backpack 1, 2, and 3 are similar. Corresponding angles on all three trapezoids are equal. The scale factor from Backpack 1 to Backpack 2 is 2. The scale factor from Backpack 1 to Backpack 3 is 1. These two backpacks are identical, only the position of the backpack on the grid changes.

**10. a.** $\left(\frac{1}{3}x, \frac{1}{3}y\right)$ **b.** $(3x, 3y)$ **c.** 3

**11. a.** No. You need to know the angle measures, so you can see if corresponding angles have equal measure. This is necessary to determine if two shapes are similar. The relationship between corresponding sides is not enough by itself.

**b. i.** $AB$ to $EF$: 6 to 4; $BC$ to $FG$: 9 to 6; $CD$ to $GH$: 12 to 8; $AD$ to $EH$: 6 to 4

   **ii.** Possible answers:

   $\frac{6}{12} = \frac{4}{8}; \frac{6}{6} = \frac{4}{4}; \frac{9}{9} = \frac{6}{6}; \frac{9}{12} = \frac{6}{8}$

   The ratios are equivalent.

   **iii.** The scale factor from polygon $ABCD$ to polygon $EFGH$ is $\frac{2}{3}$.

   The scale factor from $EFGH$ (small) to $ABCD$ (large) in 1.5.

# Stretching and Shrinking Assessment Answers (continued)

**12. a.** No, the base and height of the frame cannot be multiplied by the same scale factor to get a 6 centimeter by 4 centimeter frame.

**b.** Yes, the base and height of the frame can be multiplied by $\frac{1}{2}$ to get a 4 centimeter by 3 centimeter frame.

**13. a.** Triangle $ABC$ and Triangle $ADE$ are similar because the corresponding angles in both triangles are congruent and the corresponding ratios of the sides are equivalent. Scale factor is 2.

**b.** 12 units    **c.** 5 units

**14.** 12 ft; $\frac{x}{4} = \frac{7.5}{2.5}$ so $x = 12$

## Question Bank

**1.** $\frac{6}{9}$

**2.** rectangle A

**3.** Students can draw any shape in three similar versions (such as by using scale factors of 1, 2, and 3). Possible explanation: I know the shapes are similar, because there is a constant ratio between pairs of corresponding sides and because corresponding angles are equal.

**4. a.** The horizontal lengths would increase by a factor of 3, and the vertical lengths would increase by a factor of 6.

**b.** The figure would stay the same size, but it would move to the right 2 units and up 1 unit.

**c.** The figure would increase by a scale factor of 2 and would move up 5 units.

**5.** $a = 15, b = 15$

**6.** (Figure 3)

**7.** lengths of corresponding sides (if the scale factor is not 1), area (they will differ as the square of the scale factor)

**8. a.** The area is $1.5^2 = 2.25$ times as great.

**b.** The perimeter is 1.5 times as great.

**9.** The flagpole measures $\frac{600}{100} \times 150 = 900$ cm.

**10. a.** $(2x, 2y)$

**b.** They are similar, because all corresponding sides increased by a scale factor of 2 and corresponding angles are equal.

**11. a.**

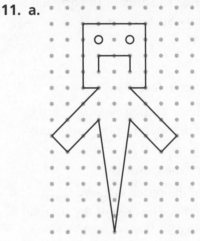

**b.** The rule must be of the form $(nx, ny)$, such as $(2x, 2y)$ or $(3x, 3y)$.

**c.** Corresponding angles are equal and the ratios of corresponding sides are equal.

**d.** The rule must be of the form $(ax, by)$, where $a \neq b$, such as $(x, 3y)$ or $(2x, y)$.

**e.** The lengths of corresponding sides are not the same ratio, corresponding angles are not equal, and the basic shape is not the same.

**12.** Sails B, E, G, and H are similar to Gilligan's sail. Possible explanation: The scale factor from Gilligan's sail to sail B is $\frac{1}{3}$, to sail E is 2, to sail G is $\frac{2}{3}$, and to sail H is 1.

**Figure 3**

| Rectangle | Scale Factor | Short Side | Long Side | Perimeter | Area |
|-----------|--------------|------------|-----------|-----------|------|
| A | 1 | 1 | 4 | 10 | 4 |
| B | 3 | 3 | 12 | 30 | 36 |
| C | 10 | 10 | 40 | 100 | 400 |
| D | $\frac{1}{2}$ | $\frac{1}{2}$ | 2 | 5 | 1 |

# Comparing and Scaling Assessment Answers

## Check-Up

The problems in this Check-Up were designed to be answered with the use of a calculator.

1. a. Possible answer: Students prefer water to juice during the game by a ratio of 40 to 10 or 4 to 1.

   b. Possible answer: 58.3% of the students prefer a sports beverage to the other drinks during the game.

2. a. Possible answer: $\frac{2}{3}$ of the students prefer juice to the other drinks after the game.

   b. Possible answer: 20 fewer students prefer a sports beverage to water after the game.

3. a. 70 to 40

   b. 35 to 20, 140 to 80, 175 to 100, or 7 to 4

4. a. Not accurate. The ratio should be 10 to 40 or 1 to 4 OR the order of the ratio should be switched to "water to juice."

   b. Accurate.

   c. Accurate.

5. a. 198

   b. A ratio, percent, fraction, or difference may be used as long as the explanation is reasonable.

## Partner Quiz

1. $10.43; 4 burgers cost $1.39, 1 burger costs $0.3475, 30 burgers × $0.3475/burger = $10.425, or $10.43 OR $\frac{30 \text{ burgers}}{4 \text{ per pound}}$ = 7.5 pounds, 7.5 pounds × $1.39/pound = $10.425, or $10.43

2. $14.97; 10 patties for $4.99; 30 patties for $14.97

3. Bulky; at Streamline, 6 cans cost $1.99, so 24 cans for $7.96; at Bulky, 24 cans cost $6.99

4. Streamline OR buying from both; at Streamline, 8 buns cost $1.49, so 32 buns cost $5.96 while at Bulky, 12 buns cost $2.09, so 36 buns cost $6.27; two 12-packs from Bulky for $4.18 + one 8-pack from Streamline for $1.49 = 32 buns for $5.67.

5. If students buy the same item at different stores to save as much as possible, see Figure 1. $\frac{\$51.39}{30 \text{ people}}$ = $1.713, or about $1.72 per person.

   If students do not think they can buy the same item at different stores to save as much as possible, see Figure 2 on the next page. $\frac{\$53.04}{30 \text{ people}}$ = $1.768, or about $1.77 per person.

**Figure 1**

|  | Streamline | Bulky | # of items | Cost |
|---|---|---|---|---|
| Cola | one 6-pack for $1.99 | one 24-pack for $6.99 | 30 | $8.98 |
| Burger | 30 burgers cost $10.43 | 30 patties for $14.97 | 30 | $10.43 |
| Buns | one 8-pack of buns for $1.49 | two 12-packs of buns for $4.18 | 32 | $5.67 |
| Chips | 6 bags at $0.89 each for $5.34 | three 8-packs for $20.97 | 30 | $26.31 |
|  |  |  | Total | $51.39 |

# Comparing and Scaling Assessment Answers *(continued)*

## Multiple-Choice Items

1. B      2. H      3. A
4. J      5. B      6. H

## Unit Test

The problems in this Unit Test were designed to be answered with the use of a calculator.

1. **a.** Red: 1 ticket for $0.75; Blue: 1 ticket for $0.80; Yellow: 1 ticket for $1.00
   **b.** 50 tickets for $37.50 → 10 Tickets for $7.50 → 40 Tickets for $30 OR $0.75 per ticket × 40 tickets = $30
   **c.** 20 tickets for $16 → 10 tickets for $8 → 5 tickets for $4 → 25 tickets for $20 OR $\frac{\$20}{\$0.80 \text{ per ticket}} = 25$ tickets

2. **a.** 3 miles per 20 minutes = 0.15 miles per minute
   **b.** 3 miles per 20 minutes → 9 miles per 60 minutes = 9 mph OR 1.15 miles per minute × 60 minutes = 9 mph
   **c.** $d = 9t$
   **d.** 3 miles per 20 min → 6 miles per 40 min → $\frac{3}{4}$ mile per 5 min → $6\frac{3}{4}$ mile per 45 min OR 0.15 miles per minute × 45 minutes = 6.75 miles

3. **a.** Students may write different proportions: $\frac{64}{16} = \frac{x}{5}$ OR $\frac{16}{64} = \frac{5}{x}$ OR $\frac{5}{16} = \frac{x}{64}$ OR $\frac{16}{5} = \frac{64}{x}$. Suppose they write
   $$\frac{64}{16} = \frac{x}{5}$$
   then $\frac{4}{1} = \frac{x}{5}$
   so $x = 20$
   **b.** $\frac{64 \text{ pretzels}}{16 \text{ ounces}} = 4$ pretzels per ounce
   **c.** $\frac{64 \text{ pretzels}}{16 \text{ ounces}} = \frac{1 \text{ pretzel}}{0.25 \text{ ounce}}$

4. Many different comparison statements are possible. Two examples are given.
   (1) Kathy gave away more balloons than Linda by a ratio of 25 to 16.
   (2) Kathy gave away 61% of the total balloons given away.

5. **a.** $\frac{\$156}{2 \text{ weeks}} = \$78$ per week = $4,056.00 per 52 weeks
   **b.** $78 per 1 week = $78 per 12 hours, so Kelsey makes $6.50 per hour
   **c.** $\frac{\$2,220}{\$78} \approx 28.21$ weeks. So, Kelsey needs about 29 weeks to have enough for the car.

6. 2.22 feet wide

**Figure 2**

|  | Streamline | Bulky | # of items | Cost |
|---|---|---|---|---|
| **Cola** | five 6-packs = 30 cans for $9.95 | two 24-packs = 48 cans for $13.98 | 30 | $9.95 |
| **Burger** | 30 burgers cost $10.43 | 30 patties for $14.97 | 30 | $10.43 |
| **Buns** | four 8-packs = 32 buns for $5.96 | three 12-packs = 36 buns for $6.27 | 32 | $5.96 |
| **Chips** | 30 bags at $0.89 each for $26.70 | four 8-packs = 32 bags for $27.96 | 30 | $26.70 |
|  |  |  | **Total** | **$53.04** |

# Comparing and Scaling Assessment Answers *(continued)*

## Question Bank

1. Since 2 out of 5 students are girls, the school has $\frac{2}{5} \times 623$ = about 249 girls.

2. $\frac{623}{25}$ = about 25 teachers

3. **a.** $0.45 per donut
   **b.** about 2.2 donuts, or 2 since you cannot cut them up in the store, for $1

4. **a.** pencils per dollar; dollar amount per pencil
   **b.** 8 pencils for $1 tells you how many pencils you could buy with $1; $0.13 per pencil tells you how much each pencil costs

5. **a.** $x = 16$        **b.** $x = 24$
   **c.** $x = 1$          **d.** $x = 9$
   **e.** $x = 15$        **f.** $x = 21$

6. **a.** At an average of 8.5 candies per small package, and noting that a 2-lb bag holds the same amount as 16 small packages, Kaitlyn can expect about $8.5 \times 16 = 136$ pieces of candy.
   **b.** It would take $64 \div 2 = 32$ small packages (at a cost of $4.00) or two 32-oz bags (at a cost of $5.58), so it would cost $1.58 less to buy the 2-oz packages.

7. **a.** The Giant Foot (with an area of $2 \times 12 \times 12 = 288$ in$^2$) is $\frac{288 \text{ in}^2}{\$8.99} = 32.0$ in$^2$ per dollar, while two Wee Czar's pizzas (with an area of $2 \times \pi \times 36 = 226$ in$^2$) is $\frac{226 \text{ in}^2}{\$8.88} = 25.5$ in$^2$ per dollar, so the Giant Foot gives you more pizza for your money.
   **b.** Since $\frac{288}{226}$ = about 1.27, the Giant Foot is actually about 27% larger than two Wee Czar's pizzas.

8. The 2-L bottles are $\frac{8 \text{ L}}{\$4.99} = 1.6$ L per dollar, and the $\frac{1}{2}$-L bottles are $\frac{4 \text{ L}}{\$1.99} = 2.0$ L per dollar, so the 8-pack of $\frac{1}{2}$-L bottles is the better buy.

9. **a.** Possible answer: The earth's water surface is about 2.4 times its land surface.
   **b.** About $\frac{139,000,000}{196,900,000} = 70.6\%$ of the earth's surface is water.
   **c.** Answers will vary. For example: South Dakota has a total area of 77,121 mi$^2$, so the earth's surface area is about $196,900,000 \div 77,121 = 2,553$ times that of South Dakota's.

10. (Figure 3) The table shows the unit price for each item at each store. Darren's has the best unit price on handkerchiefs, greeting cards, and audiocassette tapes; ballpoint pens cost essentially the same at the two stores. (Students may argue that pens are cheaper at U-Rule; a point that should be discussed is that the difference is negligible unless a large quantity is purchased.)

11. It is about 13.5 cm from Seattle to New York, or $13.5 \times 195 = 2,630$ miles. If there were a direct road, it would take $\frac{2,630}{55} \approx 48$ hours to drive from Seattle to New York. Since there is no direct road, it will take longer.

**Figure 3**

| Item | Darren's Warehouse | U-Rule Department Store |
|---|---|---|
| handkerchiefs | $1.10 | $1.25 |
| greeting cards | 1.25 | 1.83 |
| ballpoint pens | 0.80 | 0.795 |
| audiocassette tapes | 1.10 | 1.19 |

12. Possible answer: From Seattle to Los Angeles, it is 4.9 cm $\times$ 195 mi/cm = about 956 mi, so it would take the plane about $\frac{956}{500}$ = about 2 h.

13. Possible answer: From Columbus, Ohio (near the center of the state), it is about 7.2 cm $\times$ 195 mi/cm = 1,404 mi to Chihuahua.

14. *Titanic* earned about $\frac{600}{360} = \frac{5}{3}$ or 1.67 times what *Jurassic Park* earned.

15. *Star Wars Episode IV* earned about $\frac{460}{4,200} \approx \frac{1}{9}$ of the total earnings of the top 10 movies.

16. *Titanic* earned about $\frac{600}{400} = \frac{3}{2}$ of the amount earned by *Spider-Man*.

17. *E.T. The Extra-Terrestrial* earned about $\frac{435}{4,248} \approx 0.10$ of the total earnings of the top 10 movies.

18. Possible answers: There was an increase over a third of a million people (352,168).

    As a ratio, there was about a $\frac{352,168}{9,519,338}$ = 3.7% increase.

19. The population of Maricopa County increased by $\frac{317,111}{3,072,149}$ = about 10.3%.

20. Wayne County had a 1.6% decrease, Cuyahoga County had a 2.2% decrease, and Allegheny County had a 1.6% decrease.

21. Possible answer: Comparing 2 planets, Earth takes about 4 times as long as Mercury to circle the sun.

22. Possible answer: Earth and Mars take about same amount of time to turn on their axes.

23. a. Sun's diameter: $\frac{865,000}{7,926}$ = about 109 in.

    b. Jupiter diameter: $\frac{88,846}{7,926}$ = about 11.2 in.

    c. Pluto's diameter: $\frac{1,485}{7,926}$ = about 0.19 in.

    d. Mercury: $\frac{36}{12}$ = 3 ft

    e. Earth: $\frac{93}{12}$ = 7.75 ft

    f. Pluto: $\frac{3,647}{12}$ = 304 ft

# Accentuate the Negative Assessment Answers

## Partner Quiz

1. (Figure 1)
2. a. $^-250 + 175 = ^-75$
   b. $^-75 + 200 - 125 = 0$ OR
      $^-75 + 200 + ^-125 = 0$
   c. $0 + 125 = 125$
   d. $125 - 150 + 60 = 35$ OR
      $125 + ^-150 + 60 = 35$
3. a. $^-22$      b. 8
   c. $^-10$      d. $^-12$
4. (Figure 2)
5. $24 - ^-11 = n$

## Check-Up

1. $^-6.8 \times 3 = ^-20.4$
   $225 - 20.4 = 204.6$ pounds left.
2. a. $32 + 5 \times 6 = \$62$ or
      $^-32 - (5 \times 6) = ^-62$
   b. $32 \div 6 = 5\frac{1}{3}$ months,
      or 5 months and 10 days.
3. $^-3$   4. 3   5. $^-1$   6. 19
7. 4   8. $^-150$   9. 60   10. $^-9$

## Multiple-Choice Items

1. B    2. H    3. B    4. J
5. A    6. G    7. C    8. F

## Unit Test

1. $^-\frac{3}{2}, ^-\frac{9}{8}, 0, \frac{2}{5}, \frac{8}{7}$
2. a. 47      b. 13
   c. $^-75$      d. $^-12$
   e. $^-29$      f. $\frac{1}{4}$
3. $^-61$
4. a. $62 - n = ^-8$ and $62 - ^-8 = n$
   b. $70 = n$
5. a. $^-91$      b. 160
   c. $^-33$      d. 3
   e. 0      f. $\frac{-5}{21}$
6. a. $43.75
   b. $5 \cdot 5.50 + 5 \cdot 3.25 = 43.75$ OR
      $5(5.50 + 3.25) = 43.75$
   c. Possible answers:
      Using the Commutative Property to
      rewrite the sentence,
      $5 \cdot 5.50 + 5 \cdot 3.25 = 5 \cdot 3.25 + 5 \cdot 5.50$
      OR
      $5(5.50 + 3.25) = 5(3.25 + 5.50)$
      Using the Distributive Property to
      rewrite the sentence,
      $5(5.50 + 3.25) = 5 \cdot 5.50 + 5 \cdot 3.25$
7. a. $=$    b. $\neq$    c. $=$    d. $\neq$

Figure 1

Figure 2    **January Temperatures in Portland, Maine**

| Temperature at 8:00 A.M. | Temperature at 8:00 P.M. | Change in Temperature From 8:00 A.M. to 8 P.M. |
|---|---|---|
| $-8°$ | $3°$ | **11°** |
| $-2°$ | $-13°$ | **−11°** |
| $-13°$ | $-2°$ | $11°$ |
| $-1°$ | $14°$ | $15°$ |
| $6°$ | $-2°$ | $-8°$ |
| $-9°$ | $-5°$ | $4°$ |

# Accentuate the Negative Assessment Answers (continued)

**8.**

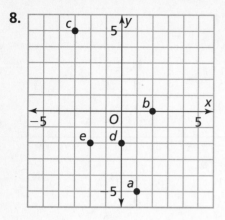

**9. a.** $(17 + 0 + {}^-9 + {}^-3 + 10) \div 5 =$
$(15) \div 5 = 3°$
**b.** $17 - {}^-9 = 26°$

## Question Bank

**1. a.** less than 500 pounds
**b.** 2 pounds less (or $^-2$ pounds)
**2. a.** less than 800 pounds
**b.** 5 pounds less (or $^-5$ pounds)
**3.** (Note: Numbers should be from $^-10$ to 10, no number should be repeated, and the numbers must total $^-11$).
Possible answers: $^-1, {}^-2, {}^-3, {}^-4, {}^-6, {}^+5$ or $^-10, {}^-9, {}^-1, {}^+2, {}^+3, {}^+4$
**4.** $10 + 10 + 10 = 30$
$10 + {}^-5 + {}^-5 = 0$
$10 + 10 + 1 = 21$
$1 + 1 + 1 = 3$
$10 + 10 + {}^-5 = 15$
$1 + 1 + {}^-5 = {}^-3$
$10 + 1 + 1 = 12$
$1 + {}^-5 + {}^-5 = {}^-9$
$10 + 1 + {}^-5 = 6$
$^-5 + {}^-5 + {}^-5 = {}^-15$
**5.** true; Possible explanation: If you have a negative number on a chip board (for example, 5 reds) and you add more negatives (3 more reds), you will have a negative (8 reds).
**6.** false; Possible explanation: If you have a positive number of groups of negatives on a chip board (for example, 5 groups of negative 3), then the total is 15 negative

chips, or $-15$. If you change the positive number to a negative, than you have the opposite. So $(-5) \times (-3)$ is the opposite of $(5) \times (-3)$. So $(-5) \times (-3) = 15$.
**7.** false; Possible explanation: Whether the sum is positive or negative depends on which of the two numbers has the greater absolute value.
**8.** true; Possible explanation: You can think of multiplying a negative by a positive as adding the same negative integer together the number of times indicated by the positive integer.
**9.** $^-4$ and $^-5$ ($^-4 + {}^-5 = {}^-9$ and $^-4 - {}^-5 = 1$)
**10. a–c.** (Figure 3, next page)
   **d–e.** (Figure 4, next page)
   **f.** This triangle will have the same orientation as the original, but the side lengths will be three times as long.
   **g.** This triangle will have lengths three times as long as the original's but will be in quadrant III. (Note: This could also be called a 180° rotation.)
   **h.** This triangle will have lengths three times as long as the original's but will be in quadrant II. (Note: This is a reflection across the y-axis.)
**11.** $^-9°, {}^-2°, {}^-1°, 0°, 1°, 8°, 14°$
**12. a.** $6 + 22 = 28°$
   **b.** $6 - 7 = {}^-1°$
**13. a.** $^-6 + 13 = 7°$
   **b.** $^-6 - 15 = {}^-21°$
**14. a.** 10 yards gained ($^+10$)
   **b.** 30 yards gained ($^+30$)
**15.** $5.8 \times 7 = 40.6; 72 - 40.6 =$
   31.4 centimeters of snow
**16.** Possible answers: $^-1001, {}^-1003, {}^-1000.2$
**17. a.** 450 points; $650 - 200 = 450$
   **b.** 800 points; $650 - {}^-150 = 800$
   **c.** 350 points; $200 - {}^-150 = 350$
**18.** 35          **19.** 20          **20.** 17
**21.** $^-9$      **22.** 9      **23.** 22      **24.** $^-22$
**25.** $^-174$      **26.** 189      **27.** 24      **28.** $^-8$

**Figure 3**

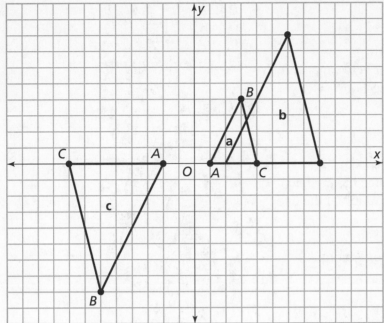

**Figure 4**

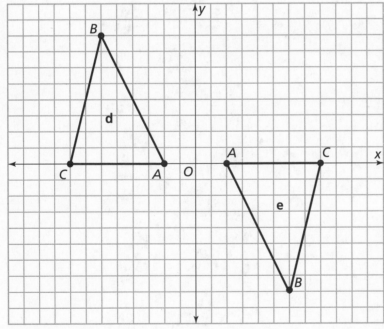

**29. a.** $^-7 \times \,^-1.5 = 10.5°$
   **b.** $6 \times \,^-1.5 = \,^-9°$
   **c.** $6 \div 1.5 = 4$ hours ago
   **d.** $8 \div 1.5 = 5\frac{1}{3}$ hours; or between 5 and 6 hours from now; or 5 hours, 20 minutes from now

**30. a.** floor 7
   **b.** floor $^-8$
   **c.** They are both 3 floors from $^-2$

**31.** Since $^-6.8 \times 3 = \,^-20.4$, the bakery had $225 - 20.4 = 204.6$ pounds left at the end of three days.

**32. a.** $32 + 6 \times 5 = \$62$ in debt
   **b.** $32 \div 6 = 5\frac{1}{3}$ months; or 5 months, 10 days

**33. a.** 6
   **b.** $^-61$
   **c.** $^-6$
   **d.** 10
   **e.** $^-14$

**34. a.** $^-2 \cdot \,^-8 + \,^-2 \cdot 5 = 6$
   **b.** $^-7 (^-2 - \,^-12) = \,^-70$
   **c.** $x \cdot 9 + x \cdot \,^-5 = 9x + \,^-5x = 4x$

**35.**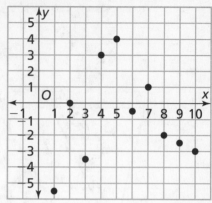

**36. a.** $56 \times (115 + \,^-15)$
   OR
   $56 \times 100$
   **b.** $(10 \times \,^-6) - (10 \times 3)$

# Moving Straight Ahead Assessment Answers

## Check-Up 1

1. **a.** Tables 2 and 3
   **b.** For Table 2: $y = 10x$
   For Table 3: $y = 10 - 2x$
2. **a.** For $y = x + 50$, as $x$ increases by one unit, $y$ increases by one unit.
   **b.** For $y = {}^-5x + 10$, as $x$ increases by one unit, $y$ decreases by 5 units.
3. For the graph on the left as $x$ increases by 1, $y$ increases by 5 and for the second graph as $x$ changes by 1, $y$ increases by 20.
4. Yes; since as $x$ increases by one $y$ increases by 15. There is a constant rate of change.

## Partner Quiz

1. **a.** Possible answer: The scale should make the hourly rate reasonable. Assuming Jake makes about $4.50 per hour, the graph looks like this:

   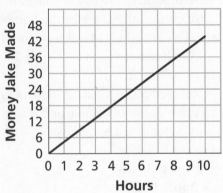

   **Jake's Babysitting**

   **b.** Answers will vary. For the example given in part (a), the equation is $y = 4.5x$.
   **c.** If the line were steeper, it would mean that Jake makes more money per hour. Answers for the equation may vary, but one possibility is that a generous friend gives him $10 per hour. The equation would be $y = 10x$.
2. **a.** 250 gallons are being pumped out of Rachel's pool per hour. We see this because every time one hour passes, W decreases by 250. We could also

make a table of values or a graph and see the same thing.

   **b.** After 11 hours, $9000 - 250\,(11) =$ 6,250 gallons are left in the pool. Students may see this with a table, a graph, or with the equation $W = -250\,(11) + 9{,}000$.
   **c.** 9000 gallons were in the pool at the start, since when $t = 0$, $W = 9{,}000$.
   **d.** Students can see this with a table, graph, or equation. To use an equation, set $W = 0$ and solve for $t$.
   $$9{,}000 - 250t = 0$$
   $$t = 36$$
   It will take 36 hours for the pool to empty.
3. Again, this problem can be solved using a graph, a table, or an equation. One way is to look at Jabal's distance from home and Michael's distance from Jabal's home. When the two distances are equal, Jabal and Michael will meet. Notice that it is not enough to look at when Jabal and Michael are the same distance from their respective homes, because they are traveling at different speeds. They will meet slightly closer to Jabal's house.
   Jabal's distance from his own house is $y = 2x$. Michael's distance from Jabal's house is $y = 20 - 2.5x$.
   Setting up a graph or table and looking for when the $y$-values are equal requires some work because the answer is not a whole number.

| $x$ | $y_J$ | $y_M$ |
|---|---|---|
| 0 | 0 | 20 |
| 1 | 2 | 17.5 |
| 2 | 4 | 15 |
| 3 | 6 | 12.5 |
| 4 | 8 | 10 |
| 5 | 10 | 7.5 |

This table gives an answer between 4 and 5 seconds.

Using a symbolic method, we ask: for what $x$ are the two distances equal? We solve for $x$ in the following equation:

$2x = 20 - 2.5x$
$4.5x = 20$
$x \approx 4.44$

In other words, after approximately 4.44 seconds, the two boys are at the same place.
This is $2(4.44) = 8.88$ meters from Jabal's house.

## Check-Up 2

**1. a.** $y = 6$; Student may make a table for this equation or may substitute the value for $x$ in the equation.

 **b.** $x = 6.25$; Student may make a table for this equation or may substitute the value for $y$ in the equation and solve for $x$.

**2. a.** $x = 3$  **b.** $x = 3$
 **c.** $x = 6$  **d.** $x = 2$

**3. a.** To find out when the revenue (income) and cost are equal, we find $x$ so that $5.50x = 250 + 1.25x$. To solve by graphing, draw the two linear graphs and find their point of intersection (student will have to estimate the actual intersection point). To solve symbolically:
$5.50x = 250 + 1.25x$
$x \approx 58.8$, so about 59 bouquets.
When they sell 59 bouquets, the cost and revenue will both be approximately $324. Students may also write that if they sell 58 bouquets, they will have a slight loss, and if they sell 59 bouquets, they will make a slight profit.

 **b.** The $y$-intercept for the revenue equation is $(0, 0)$ because if the store sells no bouquets, they will make no money. The $y$-intercept for the cost equation is $(0, 250)$ because even if the store does not sell a single bouquet, the operation will cost them $250.

 **c.** The constant rate of change for revenue is 5.5. This means that for each bouquet they sell, they will bring in $5.50. The constant rate of change for cost is 1.25, which means that each bouquet will cost an additional $1.25 over the original start-up cost.

## Multiple Choice

**1.** B  **2.** F  **3.** B  **4.** H
**5.** C  **6.** H  **7.** D

## Unit Test

**1. a.** No. Rate of change is constant. For example, the slope of the line between $(0, {}^-2)$ and $(1, 1)$ is 3, as is the slope of the line between $(1, 1)$ and $(2, 4)$.

 **b.** $y = 3x - 2$

**2.** Note: students are asked to form groups so the naming of each group is arbitrary. The matches are as follows:
Group 1: A-F-K
Group 2: B-H-M
Group 3: C-G-J
Group 4: D-E-L

**3. a.** $x = 1$  **b.** $x = {}^-5$
 **c.** $x = 5$  **d.** $x = 3$

**4. a.** He might be trying to determine how long it would take before a walker was 216 meters from the start

OR

how far the walker was from the start after 88 seconds.

**b.** To solve the problem of finding how long it would take before the walker was 216 meters from the start, the equation would be $216 = 40 + 2x$.

OR

To solve the problem of finding how far the walker was from the start after 88 seconds, the equation would be $y = 40 + 2(88)$.

**5. a.**

#### Movie Memberships

| N | 0 | 10 | 20 | 30 | 40 | 50 |
|---|---|----|----|----|----|----|
| $C_1$ | 75 | 95 | 115 | 135 | 155 | 175 |
| $C_2$ | 0 | 57.50 | 115 | 172.50 | 230 | 287.50 |

**b.**

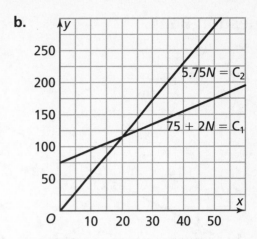

**c.** $C_1 = 75 + 2N$, $C_2 = 5.75N$

**d.** The slope of the member line is 2 and the slope of the nonmember line is 5.75.

**e.** The slope is the cost per movie.

**f.** Table: You can look at the change per unit of movies.

Graph: Look at the ratio of change in rise to change in run.

Equation: Read off the answers as the coefficient of $x$.

**g.** The $y$-intercept is just how much a member or nonmember has to pay if they do not go to any movies at all.

# Moving Straight Ahead Assessment Answers *(continued)*

## Question Bank

**1. a.**

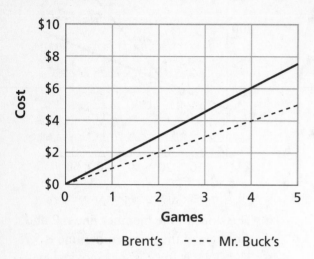

Brent's ——— Mr. Buck's - - - -

**b.** Possible answer: Brent might charge a membership fee of $5 and then $.50 per game per night. For the first 10 games, Brent's customers will pay more, but after 10 games their total cost will be lower than if they rented from Mr. Buck's. Brent should advertise his plan, emphasizing that if you are a frequent customer you will be better off at Brent's.

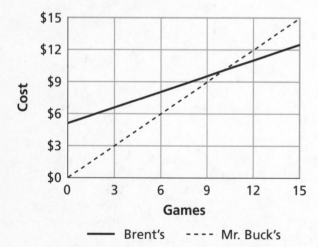

Brent's ——— Mr. Buck's - - - -

**2.** On the appropriate screen you need to enter the equations $Y_1 = 300 + 20X$ and $Y_2 = 50 + 35X$, where X represents the number of bikes. Next you need to set a window appropriate for the context, maybe $x$ values from 0 to 20 and $y$ values corresponding to these, say from 0 to 700. When you graph these equations, you will see two lines giving the costs for the two companies. The point where the lines cross is the point where the two plans cost the same for that number of bikes. Before or after that point, one company or the other has the better deal.

**3.** You can think of solving an equation like this one as reversing the procedure that was done to create the expression on the left. To make $4n - 7$ you would multiply $n$ by 4 and then subtract 17. To reverse this, you add 17, then divide by 4.

$$4n - 17 = 43$$
$$4n - 17 + 17 = 43 + 17$$
$$4n = 60$$
$$\frac{4n}{4} = \frac{60}{4}$$
$$n = 15$$

**4. a.**

| x | −3 | −2 | −1 | 0 | 1 |
|---|----|----|----|---|---|
| y | −2 | 0 | 2 | 4 | 6 |

**b.** slope $= \frac{2}{1} = 2$, $y$-intercept $= 4$

**5.** (Figure 1, next page)

**a.** The $y$-intercepts are 8, ⁻3, and 1.

**b.** The slopes are ⁻3, 4, and $\frac{1}{3}$.

# Moving Straight Ahead Assessment Answers *(continued)*

**Figure 1**

|  | Table | Graph | Equation |
|---|---|---|---|

### Row 1

| x | y |
|---|---|
| −2 | 14 |
| 0 | 8 |
| 1 | 5 |
| 2 | 2 |
| 3 | −1 |

$y = -3x + 8$

### Row 2

| x | y |
|---|---|
| 0 | −3 |
| 1 | 1 |
| 2 | 5 |

$y = 4x - 3$

### Row 3

| x | y |
|---|---|
| −2 | $\frac{1}{3}$ |
| −1 | $\frac{2}{3}$ |
| 0 | 1 |
| 1 | $1\frac{1}{3}$ |
| 2 | $1\frac{2}{3}$ |

$y = \frac{1}{3}x + 1$

**6. a.**

Table A

| Diff. x | x | y | Diff. y |
|---|---|---|---|
| | −2 | −1 | |
| 1 | −1 | 1 | 2 |
| 1 | 0 | 3 | 2 |
| 1 | 1 | 5 | 2 |
| 1 | 2 | 7 | 2 |

Table B

| Diff. x | x | y | Diff. y |
|---|---|---|---|
| | −3 | −8 | |
| 2 | −1 | 0 | 8 |
| 2 | 1 | 0 | 0 |
| 2 | 3 | −8 | −8 |
| 2 | 5 | −24 | −16 |

Table C

| Diff. x | x | y | Diff. y |
|---|---|---|---|
| | −3 | $-\frac{1}{2}$ | |
| 2 | −1 | $\frac{1}{2}$ | 1 |
| 1 | 0 | 1 | $\frac{1}{2}$ |
| 3 | 3 | 2.5 | 1.5 |
| 2 | 5 | 3.5 | 1 |

Table D

| Diff. x | x | y | Diff. y |
|---|---|---|---|
| | −2 | −5 | |
| 1 | −1 | −3 | 2 |
| 1 | 0 | −1 | 2 |
| 1 | 1 | 1 | 2 |
| 1 | 2 | 3 | 2 |

**b.** In tables A and D, both $x$ and $y$ increase by constant amounts. The ratios of these amounts, change in $y$: change in $x$, is always constant (2:1 for table A and table D).

In table B, $x$-values increase by increments of 2, but $y$-values increase and then decrease, making first positive changes, then negative changes. The ratio, change in $y$: change in $x$, is not a constant.

In table C, $x$ and $y$ do not increase by constant amounts. However, change in $y$: change in $x$ is always 1:2.

**c.** table A: $y = 2x + 3$

table C: $y = \frac{1}{2}x + 1$

table D: $y = 2x - 1$

**d.** Adrian added the columns to help her look at how the increments in the $y$ values changed in relation to how the increments in the $x$ values changed. In linear relationships, the ratio of these changes will be constant. Once Adrian had determined which of the tables represented linear relationships, she could find the related equations, because the ratio of the increments is the slope of the line.

**7. a.** $n = 4t - 160 = 4(90) - 160 = 360 - 160 = 200$ chirps per minute

**b.**
$$48 = 4t - 160$$
$$48 + 160 = 4t - 160 + 160$$
$$208 = 4t$$
$$\frac{208}{4} = \frac{4t}{4}$$
$$52 = t$$

The temperature is 52°F.

# Filling and Wrapping Assessment Answers

## Check-Up 1

1. **a.** Surface Area = 306 in.$^2$
   **b.** Volume = 270 in.$^3$
2. **a.** The 16 by 1 by 1 box would require 66 in.$^2$ of cardboard.
   **b.** The 4 by 2 by 2 box would require 40 in.$^2$ of cardboard.
3. **a.** Answers will vary. Possible pattern:

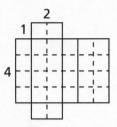

   **b.** Volume = $1 \times 2 \times 4 = 8$ cubic inches
   **c.** Surface Area
   $= 2(1 \times 2) + 2(2 \times 4) + 2(1 \times 4)$
   $= 28$ square inches

## Partner Quiz

1. $2(2.75^2 \times \pi) + 5.5\pi \times 8.25 \approx 190$ in.$^2$
2. $2(11^2 \times \pi) + 22\pi \times 33 \approx 3041$ in.$^2$
3. $2.75^2 \times \pi \times 8.25 \approx 196$ in.$^3$
4. $11^2 \times \pi \times 33 \approx 12{,}544$ in.$^3$
5. The volume of the business size can is 64 times that of the home size can, so the price for the large can should be $54.40 or less.
6. Answers will vary. Possible prisms:

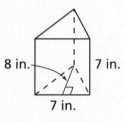

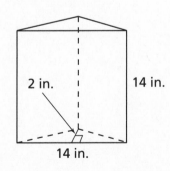

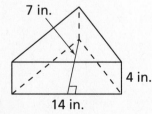

## Check-Up 2

1. $32\pi \approx 100.5$ in.$^3$
2. $\frac{1}{3} \times 100.5 \approx 33.5$ in.$^3$
3. $\frac{2}{3} \times 100.5 \approx 67$ in.$^3$
4. Approximately 33 cents
5. $\frac{2}{3}(3.5^2 \times \pi \times 7) \approx 179.59$ cm$^3$

## Multiple Choice

1. D    2. H    3. B    4. H
5. B    6. J    7. C    8. J
9. B    10. F

## Unit Test

1. $2(4 \times 6) + 2(2 \times 6) + 2 \times 4 = 80$ in.$^2$
2. $2(8 \times 12) + 2(4 \times 12) + 8 \times 4 = 320$ in.$^2$
3. $2 \times 4 \times 8 = 48$ in.$^3$
4. $4 \times 8 \times 12 = 384$ in.$^3$
5. $6.00 (8 times the price of the micro box.)
6. One way to get twice the volume of the jumbo box is to double one of the dimensions. Possible answers include: 8 by 8 by 12, 4 by 16 by 12, or 4 by 8 by 24.
7. $\frac{2}{3} \times 729 = 486$ cm$^3$
8. **a.** Yes, the two cylinders have the same volume: $(6^2 \times 5)\pi$ or $(3^2 \times 20)\pi$, both of which are $180\pi$ cm$^3$.
   **b.** No, the cylinders do not have the same surface area.
   The shorter cylinder has surface area of $132\pi \approx 414.69$ cm$^2$.
   The taller cylinder has surface area of $138\pi \approx 433.54$ cm$^2$.
9. The volume of the cylinder section is $\pi \times 5^2 \times 8 \approx 628$ ft$^3$. The volume of the cone section is $\frac{1}{3} \times 628 \approx 209$ ft$^3$. The total volume of the nose cone is approximately $628 + 209 = 837$ ft$^3$.

## Question Bank

1. Only pattern c forms a closed box. The others do not.

2. **a.** Yes. The triangular bases are isosceles right triangles. If these are placed so the hypotenuses coincide, then the two triangles form a square.

   **b.** No, the faces where the two triangular prisms are joined would not be faces of the square prism.

3. **a.** $8 \times 4 + 2 = 34$. This is the surface area of a $1 \times 1 \times 8$ prism.

   **b.** $2 \times 2 \times 2 = 8$. This is the volume of a $2 \times 2 \times 2$ rectangular prism.

   **c.** $2 \times 1 \times 4 = 8$. This is the volume of a $2 \times 1 \times 4$ rectangular prism.

   **d.** $2 \times 4 + 2 \times 4 \times 2 + 2 \times 2 = 8 + 16 + 4 = 28$. This is the surface area of a $2 \times 1 \times 4$ rectangular prism.

4. **a.** $42.65$ in.$^3$; Volume of house $= 2 \times 2 \times 4 + 2 \times 2 \times 2 + 2 \times 2 \times \left(\frac{1}{2}\right) \times 2 = 28$ cubic inches
   Volume of barn $= \pi \times 1 \times 4 + \left(\frac{1}{2}\right) \times \left(\frac{2}{3}\right) \times \pi \times 1 \times 2 = \left(4\frac{2}{3}\right)\pi \approx 14.65$ cubic inches $= (28 + 14.65)$ cubic inches $= 42.65$ cubic inches

   **b.** $56$ in.$^2$;
   $2 \times 2 \times 2 + 2 \times 4 \times 2 + 2 \times 2 + 2 \times 2 \times 4 + 2 \times 2 \times \left(\frac{1}{2}\right) \times 2 + 2 \times 2 \times 2 = 8 + 16 + 4 + 16 + 4 + 8 = 56$ in.$^2$

5. **a.** $1$ in.$^3 = 2.54$ cm$^3 = 16.39$

   **b.** $458.92$ cm$^3$

   **c.** $1$ in.$^2 = 6.45$ cm$^2$. So the surface area of an inch cube $= 6(6.45)$ cm$^2 = 38.7$ cm$^2$

   **d.** $361.2$ cm$^2$

6. **a.** $150$ cm$^2$

   **b.** $125$ cm$^3$

7. The box's volume is $1$ ft$^3$. The basketball's volume is $\frac{2}{3}$ of the volume of the box.

   Each box contains approximately $\frac{1}{3}$ ft$^3$ of foam.

8. The volume of the dirt removed is $25 \times 15 \times 3 = 1125$ m$^3$, at a cost of $\frac{4200}{1125} \approx \$3.73$ per cubic meter.

9. **a.** 15 cubes

   **b.** 7 layers

   **c.** 105 unit cubes

10. $9 \times 6\frac{1}{2} \times \frac{1}{6} = 9.75$ yd$^3$ of cement

11. The volume of the box is $343$ cm$^3$, so each edge has a length of 7 cm $(7 \times 7 \times 7 = 343)$. One face of the box has an area of $7 \times 7 = 49$, so the total surface area is $6 \times 49 = 294$ cm$^2$.

12. *volume of the container:* $\pi \times 3^2 \times 18 \approx 509$ cm$^3$,
    *volume of one tennis ball:* $\frac{4}{3} \times \pi \times 3^3 \approx 113$ cm$^3$,
    *volume of air:* $509 - (3 \times 113) = 170$ cm$^3$

13. **a.** $\frac{1}{3} \times 7 \times 3^2 \times \pi \approx 66$ cm$^3$

    **b.** $1000 \div 66 =$ about 15 cups (Students might suggest 16 or 17, reasoning that the cups would not be completely filled.)

    **c.** As $\frac{1}{3} \times \pi \times 6^2 \times 7 \approx 264$ cm$^3$, the volume is 4 times greater.

    **d.** As $\frac{1}{3} \times \pi \times 3^2 \times 14 \approx 132$ cm$^3$, the volume is 2 times greater.

    **e.** As $\frac{1}{3} \times \pi \times 6^2 \times 14 \approx 528$ cm$^3$, the volume is 8 times greater.

# What Do You Expect? Assessment Answers

## Check-Up 1

1. **a.** The probability of Sara scoring 1 point on the first draw is $\frac{12}{24} = \frac{1}{2}$.

    $P(\text{Cela}) = \frac{8}{24} = \frac{1}{3}$ and

    $P(\text{Katie}) = \frac{4}{24} = \frac{1}{6}$.

    **b.** $P(\text{not drawing Green}) = \frac{20}{24} = \frac{5}{6}$.

    **c.** The probabilities change. The total number of marbles is 30 and each number of colors increased by 2.

    $P(\text{Red}) = \frac{14}{30} < \frac{1}{2}$. $P(\text{Blue}) = \frac{10}{30} = \frac{1}{3}$.

    $P(\text{green}) = \frac{6}{30} > \frac{1}{6}$. Students may note that the probability of blue has not changed. This is because the fraction of green marbles was $\frac{1}{3}$ originally and $\frac{1}{3}$ in the newly added marbles.

    **d.** The probabilities do not change. There are 48 marbles.

    $P(\text{Red}) = \frac{24}{48} = \frac{1}{2}$.

    $P(\text{Blue}) = \frac{16}{48} = \frac{1}{3}$.

    $P(\text{green}) = \frac{8}{48} = \frac{1}{6}$.

2. **a.** From four entrees and two drinks, $4 \times 2 = 8$ different meals can be designed. Students will probably construct a list or tree to determine this: Let H stand for hamburger, D for hot dog, P for pizza, C for chicken, M for milk, and S for Soda:

### Meal Combinations

| HM | DM | PM | CM |
|----|----|----|----|
| HS | DS | PS | CS |

**b.** Of the 8 possible meals, 2 have a hamburger, a probability of $\frac{2}{8} = \frac{1}{4}$. Or, as one of the four entrees is a hamburger, and as every meal has an entree, there is a $\frac{1}{4}$ probability that a lunch will have a hamburger.

**c.** This is one of the 8 possible meals, and since they are chosen at random, each is equally likely, so the probability of any particular meal is $\frac{1}{8}$.

**d.** With a choice of two desserts, there will be twice as many combinations, for a total of 16 different meals. Some students may see this multiplicative pattern. Some may need to expand the tree or list.

## Partner Quiz

1. **a.** $P(\text{white socks}) = \frac{2}{3}$. This answer does not require the area model. For parts b–e, students might draw an area model for this problem, such as the one below.

| dark socks with pants | |
|---|---|
| white socks with jeans | white socks with shorts |

Because the probabilities of pants, shorts, and jeans are not equally likely, a tree or a list is not so useful.

**b.** $P(\text{shorts}) = \frac{1}{2}$ of $\frac{2}{3} = \frac{1}{3}$

**c.** $P(\text{dress pants}) = \frac{1}{3}$

**d.** $P(\text{jeans with dark socks}) = 0$

**e.** Yes, the three are equally likely to be worn. In the area model, each region is $\frac{1}{3}$ of the square, so each choice is equally likely.

2. **a.** $P(\text{ending in Cave A}) =$
$\frac{1}{16} + \frac{1}{16} + \frac{1}{8} + \frac{1}{12} + \frac{1}{12} = \frac{5}{12}$
$P(\text{ending in Cave B}) =$
$\frac{1}{16} + \frac{1}{16} + \frac{1}{4} = \frac{3}{8}$
$P(\text{ending in Cave C}) =$
$\frac{1}{8} + \frac{1}{12} = \frac{5}{24}$

**2. b.** Possible answer: (Figure 1)

## Check-Up 2

**1.** Possible area models:

**Two-try Free-throw Situation**

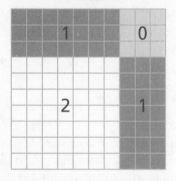

**One-and-one Free-throw Situation**

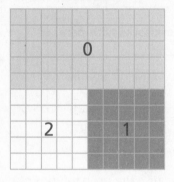

**2.** For the two-shot situation, Maribeth's average is
$(49 \times 2 + 42 \times 1 + 9 \times 0) \div 100 = 1.4$ points per trip.
For the one-and-one situation, her average is
$(25 \times 2 + 25 \times 1 + 50 \times 0) \div 100 = 0.75$ points per trip.

**3.** Maribeth can be expected to have scored $20 \times 1.4 + 30 \times 0.75 = 50.5$, or about 50 or 51, points this season.

## Multiple-Choice Items

**1.** C   **2.** H   **3.** A   **4.** H
**5.** B   **6.** G   **7.** D

## Unit Test

**1.** There are 8 possible, equally likely combinations. Students may use a tree or a list: ABA, ABA, ACA, ACA, BBA, BBA, BCA, BCA

   **a.** The probability of getting exactly 2 As is greater. The probabilities are, P(exactly 2 As) = $\frac{4}{8}$ or $\frac{1}{2}$ and P(exactly 2 Bs) = $\frac{2}{8} = \frac{1}{4}$.

   **b.** P(not getting at least one B) or P (no B's) = $\frac{2}{8}$ or $\frac{1}{4}$.

   **c.** P(none of the three sides match) = $\frac{2}{8}$ or $\frac{1}{4}$.

**Figure 1**

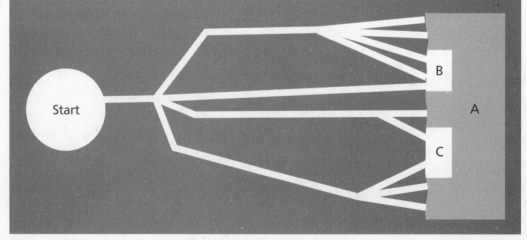

2. P (White) = $\frac{2}{3}$ of $\frac{1}{2}$ + $\frac{1}{2}$ of $\frac{1}{2}$ = $\frac{7}{12}$. Students may use an area model to find the probability.

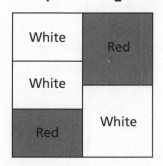

**Container 1   Container 2**

3. **a.** Students could use an area model to analyze the results of spinning each spinner once.

**Spinner B**

| Spinner A | | | |
|---|---|---|---|
| YY | YB | YR | YO |
| RY | RB | RR | RO |
| BY | BB | BR | BO |
| OY | OB | OR | OO |

If students use a list, they will have to account for the fact that the yellow region on spinner B is $\frac{1}{2}$ of the spinner, not $\frac{1}{4}$, so the four outcomes on that spinner are not equally likely. One way to do this is to imagine that spinner B is split into 6 equal-sized regions, with 3 of them being yellow.

Thinking of the problem this way, there are 4 × 6 = 24 different equally likely events with the following ones resulting in the color green: YB, BY, BY, BY.

4 of the 24 events result in the color green for a probability of $\frac{4}{24} = \frac{1}{6}$.

**b.** Spinning Spinner A twice gives a probability of making green as $\frac{2}{16}$ or $\frac{1}{8}$. Spinning Spinner B twice gives a probability of making green as $\frac{2}{12}$ or $\frac{1}{6}$. So there is no way to do better than by spinning each spinner once.

**Spinner A**

| Spinner A | | | |
|---|---|---|---|
| YY | BY | RY | OY |
| YR | BR | RR | OR |
| YB | BB | RB | OB |
| YO | BO | RO | OO |

**Spinner B**

| Spinner B | | | |
|---|---|---|---|
| YY | BY | RY | OY |
| YR | BR | RR | OR |
| YB | BB | RB | OB |
| YO | BO | RO | OO |

4. There are 8 possible arrangements of boy-girl in a 3-child family. GGG  GGB  GBG  BGG  GBB  BGB  BBG  BBB
All are equally likely assuming P(G) = $\frac{1}{2}$.
   **a.** P(GBG) = $\frac{1}{8}$
   **b.** P(exactly 2 Bs) = $\frac{3}{8}$
   **c.** (all girls) = $\frac{1}{8}$

5. **a.** P($11) = $\frac{8}{20}$ and P($2) = $\frac{12}{20}$
   Expected value is: $\left(\frac{8}{20}\right)(11) + \left(\frac{12}{20}\right)(2) = \frac{56}{10}$ = $5.60 per job
   **b.** The $6 per job is the better plan over the long run.

## Question Bank

**1. a.** $\frac{6}{20} = \frac{3}{10}$

   **b.** $\frac{14}{20} = \frac{7}{10}$

   **c.** $\frac{12}{40} = \frac{3}{10}$

   **d.** The probabilities are the same.

   **e.** $\frac{8}{28} = \frac{2}{7}$

   **f.** The probability in part *e* is less than the probability in part *a*.

   **g.** 8 blue marbles are needed to make 14 blue marbles and 14 non-blue marbles. Then P(blue) $= \frac{14}{28} = \frac{1}{2}$.

**2. a.** P(2 reds) $= \frac{1}{4}$

**second draw**

|  | R | R | W | W |
|---|---|---|---|---|
| **R** | ▨ | ▨ |  |  |
| **R** | ▨ | ▨ |  |  |
| **W** |  |  |  |  |
| **W** |  |  |  |  |

*firsf draw*

   **b.** P(2 reds) $= \frac{2}{12} = \frac{1}{6}$ (Note that the possibilities for the second draw depend on the first draw.)

**second draw**

|  |  |  |
|---|---|---|
| RR | RW | RW |
| RR | RW | RW |
| WR | WR | WW |
| WR | WR | WW |

*first draw*

**3.** They should put one red marble in one container and the remaining marbles in the other container. In this case, the probability is winning is $\frac{7}{10}$.

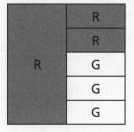

**4. a.** Spinner D; red is $\frac{1}{8}$ of the spinner, which is 12.5%. This is close to the 14% of actual spins that were red.

   **b.** $\frac{9}{16}$

**spin 2**

|  |  |  |
|---|---|---|
| | RB | RR |
| | BB | BR |

*spin 1*

**5. a.** There are one thousand possible numbers: 001 through 999, together with 000.

   **b.** $\frac{1}{1000}$

   **c.** A player could expect to *lose* $0.25 per ticket. On 1000 plays, the player can expect to win once, so the expected value is $\frac{999 \cdot 0 + 1 \cdot 750}{1000} = \$0.75$. But the player spends $1 per play, so the average loss is $0.25.

   **d.** No. States may use such lotteries in order to raise money for programs.

**6. a.**

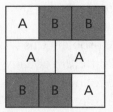

$$P(A) = \frac{19}{36}$$
$$P(B) = \frac{17}{36}$$

   **b.** Zark should expect to end in Cave A 38 times and in Cave B 34 times.

# Data Distributions Assessment Answers

## Check-Up

1. It would seem that the data are from all the middle school students in a school since there are 330 students' data reported. The students probably kept track of how much sleep they had for 1 week and then reported an average number of hours. For the number of movies and videos watched, they probably kept track of the number watched for a week and then reported the sum.

2. **a.** This distribution is skewed.

   **b.** Answers will vary. The range of the data is 0 to 50 movies and/or videos. It looks like there are some outliers (data values that are greater than 20 movies and/or videos). There are several repeated data values, particularly the data values for 0 to 5 movies and/or videos. The data cluster at the smaller numbers, with the greatest number of students watching 0 to about 5 movies and/or videos. There probably is a second, much smaller cluster at 5 to 10 movies and/or videos.

   **c.** Answers will vary. The actual median is 2 movies and/or videos. Students would need to realize that the median marks the location where the data will split evenly so there are 165 data values less than or equal to and 165 data values greater than or equal to the median. In this case, that data value is 2.

   **d.** Answers will vary. Because the distribution is skewed, we can anticipate that the mean will be larger than the median. The mean is a kind of fulcrum in a distribution so students may think about where the distribution would "balance" which is around 4 movies and/or videos (actual mean is 4.111212).

3. **a.** The distribution is bell-shaped.

   **b.** Answers will vary. The range is from 5 hours to about 12 hours. There do not appear to be any outliers. The data seem to "grow" from 5 hours to almost 8 hours. Then there are a lot of data in the interval of 8 to 9 hours sleep. It looks like there are three heavily repeated data values: 8 hours, 8.5 hours, and 9 hours. Then the data more quickly taper off to about 12 hours.

   **c.** Answers will vary. Since the distribution is bell-shaped, the median will be near the center. It appears the median might be around 8 hours. The actual median is 8.42 hours.

   **d.** Answers will vary. Since the distribution is bell-shaped, the mean will be near the center and similar to the median. Given the shape of the distribution, it appears the mean might be around 8 hours. The actual mean is 8.26491 hours.

## Partner Quiz

1. **a.** Answers will vary; the intent is for students to demonstrate that they can read the scale. The answers below are reasonable and accurate.
   Mean reaction time with DH: 0.81
   Mean reaction time with NDH: 1.05
   Median reaction time with DH: 0.79+
   Median reaction time with NDH: 1.08
   Range of reaction times for DH: 0.60, from 0.58 − 1.18
   Range of reaction times for NDH: 0.92, from 0.68 − 1.6

   **b.** Answers will vary. The ranges for the two distributions are different. For the DH, the range is about 0.6 seconds and for the NDH the range is about 1 second so there is a greater variability in NDH times. Also, the endpoints (range) are shifted higher (to the right) for NDH. About half the DH cluster from about 0.6 to 0.8 seconds. The NDH do not show such a tight cluster. The median reaction time for NDH is about two times greater than that for DH; the same appears to be true for the mean. Students seem to be twice as fast and more consistent when they use their DH when compared to their NDH.

**183**

# Data Distributions Assessment Answers *(continued)*

## Multiple Choice Items

1. A    2. J    3. B    4. J
5. B    6. H    7. D    8. G
9. C    10. J    11. A

## Unit Test Version 1

### Part I:

1. Before the assembly, the weight of backpacks varied from about 2 lb to about 22 lb. The median weight was about 11 pounds; this means that about half the students had backpacks that weighed 11 or less pounds as had backpacks that weighed 11 or more pounds. The weights of backpacks greater than the median were more spread out. Looking at backpack weights of 15 or more lbs, there were 16 students that had backpacks in this interval. This was about 20% of the 79 students. The mean and median are about 1 lb different from each other.

2. After the assembly, the weight of backpacks varied from about 3 lb to about 24 lb. The median weight was about 9 pounds; this means that about half the students had backpacks that weighed 9 or less pounds as had backpacks that weighed 9 or more pounds. The weights of backpacks greater than the median were more spread out. There were 12 students that had backpacks that weigh more than 12 pounds. This was about 10% of the 51 students. The mean and the median are about $1\frac{1}{2}$ lb different from each other. Comparing the medians and the percents of students with greater than 15 pounds, it would seem that the weights of backpacks have decreased and the numbers of students carrying heavy packs (15 lb or more) has decreased.

3. Given the response to the previous question, it would seem that the assembly did influence the students to carry less weight in their backpacks. In comparing just the medians, the "after" median is about 2 lbs less than the "before" median.

There may be other factors to consider that we don't know about here (e.g., are there some days when students seem to have to carry more "stuff" than others) but the students did use random samples and, even though the numbers in each sample were not the same, the sample sizes were okay so using both is fine.

### Part II

1. Answers will vary. The distribution after the assembly has shifted to the left so it is possible to say that the assembly had some impact.

2. Answers will vary. This is a correct statement and a reasonable analysis.

## Unit Test Version 2

### Part I

Answers will vary. A class could decide to weigh students' backpacks both before and after the assembly. A week before the assembly, they could randomly select some number of students walking in the halls before school. The students take off their backpacks so the backpacks can be weighed on a scale. The weight of each backpack is recorded to the nearest half pound.

A month later, after the assembly, the class weighs another sample of students' backpacks using the same method—stopping students in the halls before school. They try to get the same number of students as they used before.

### Part II

1. Answers will vary.
2. For parts (a)–(c) see Unit Test Version 1, Part I.

### Part III

1. Answers will vary. The distribution after the assembly has shifted to the left so it is possible to say that the assembly had some impact.

2. Answers will vary. This is a correct statement and a reasonable analysis.

# Data Distributions Assessment Answers (continued)

## Question Bank

1. The data collected in all three parts are numerical.

2. The answers to data gathered in situation (a) should be similar, while the data gathered in situations (b) and (c) should be quite varied. Student responses may vary slightly, however they should be well reasoned and consider the real life variation that may be found in each situation.

3. B

4. 72 degrees

5. The boys watched slightly more movies than the girls did in general as their mean is slightly higher than the girls. However, the difference is less than a whole movie, which is not significant. The boys also had a slightly greater range of movies watched. Most people, boys and girls, watched 3–5 movies. A few people must have watched a large number of movies.

6. a. Possible answers: The difference in means for the boys and girls is very small. The difference between the mean number of hours a boy slept and the mean number of hours a girl slept is 0.1 hour. 8% of the boys surveyed slept more than 10 hours, while only 2% of the girls surveyed slept more than 10 hours. The boys' data shows a greater range and more gaps which indicates greater variability in the data.

   b. $\frac{14}{25}$ of the boys slept more than the mean number of hours per night. 56% of the boys slept more than the mean number of hours per night.

   c. $\frac{24}{50}$ or $\frac{12}{25}$ of the girls slept more than the mean number of hours per night. 48% of the girls slept more than the mean number of hours per night.

   d. Percent would allow you to compare out of 100. Using counts would make the comparison harder.

   e. Statements ii or iii. The median is located where the data cluster. If students choose option iii, then they must have sufficient reasoning to defend their decision, such as the mean takes into account the high and the low values of the data. (mean ≈ 7.7 hours)

   f. There is not enough information given to predict with certainty any change in the median, mean, or range. However, if the sample was drawn randomly, you would not expect a significant change in the mean or the median.

7. a. His mean score would be 93 points.

   b. Possible answer: 90 points, 95 points, 98 points and 89 points.

   c. Answers will vary, for the given example in part b, the range is 9 points which tells us that his scores did not vary a great deal.

8. a. The range is 91 basketball cards, which implies that the data is fairly spread out.

   b. Each person would receive 310 cards. To find this total the individual amounts are combined and then shared equally among the five friends.

   c. The first five friends would receive fewer cards (about 302 cards per person), because Susanna's number of cards is less than the original average (310 cards).

9. None of the friends necessarily started with 364 cards. Since they divided them equally, some may have had more than 364 and others less. However there is not enough information to determine whether or not any one individual had exactly 364 cards to begin with.

10. Enrico is correct because you need to include all the data when determining the mean, even the repeated values. If you divide the total meal costs by 3 you get $5.23 per person, which is greater than any one cost of a meal and, therefore, does not make sense.

**11.** The students should disagree with John's reasoning because the total runs of all the games is considered when determining the mean number of runs per game. If you do not count the 0 runs, you divide the 33 runs by 12 games and get 2.75 runs per game. This is incorrect because 2.75 runs per game × 15 games = 41, which is greater than the total runs of John's team, 33.

**12. a.** The mean would increase because you are replacing a lower data value with a higher data value. The mean would increase by $\frac{3}{16}$ of an hour since the total hours would increase by 1.5 hours.

 **b.** The median would not change since the 4th and 5th values in the ordered data set of eight values remain at 1 hour.

 **c.** The range would not change since the smallest value would still be 0.5 and the largest value would still be 3.0.

**13. a.** Bag 1: 15% green, 18.5% yellow, 15% orange, 18.5% blue, 17% brown, and 17% red.
 Bag 2: 14.5% green, 16% yellow, 13% orange, 18% blue, 18% brown, and 20% red.

 **b.** (Figure 1, next page)

 **c.** Possible answers: The bar graph for Bag 1 is fairly flat or uniform, so the data does not vary much. The Green and Orange candies show the lowest percent in each bag. Blue, Brown and Red candies together are more than $\frac{1}{2}$ of the candies in each bag. There is less variation in percent of colors of candies in Bag 1 than in Bag 2.

 **d.** The plan appears to be for the least percent of Green and Orange candies – around 14 to 15%. The remaining colors: Yellow, Blue, Brown, and Red would be a slightly larger percent – around 18%.

**e.**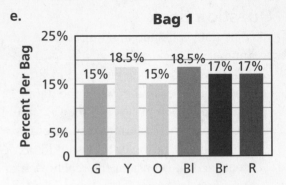

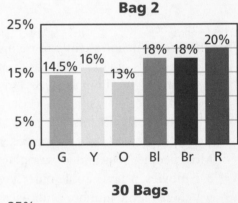

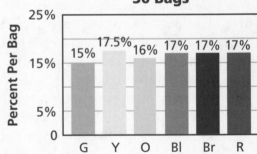

**f.** There is the same percent of blue, brown and red candies in the 30 bags. The percent of green and orange candies is slightly less in the bags. It is a pretty uniform or flat distribution.

**g.** There seems to be a general plan that the percent of colors in each bag of Crispy M&M's® candies will be between 15% and 17%. The plan might be for Green and Orange candies to be slightly less than the other four colors.

# Data Distributions Assessment Answers *(continued)*

14. **a.** The mean drops to 2.375. This happens because the sum does not change, but the number of friends increases. The median becomes 1.5 because all of the new data values are added to the left of the old median and, therefore, the new median is shifted to the left.

    **b.** The mean becomes 2.93 because the total increases and the number of people stays the same. The location of the median does not change because the stack of threes has six values to the left of it and five to the right of it. When you move one value from the left to the right of the median, it does not change because of the number of entries on 3. Notice that moving one data value to the right of the median, you now have six values to the right and five values to the left of the three on the stack of 3's, so the median is still 3.

15. Possible answers: The gymnasts' heights are clustered between 4 feet and 5 feet, while the basketball players are clustered between 5.5 feet and 6.25 feet. The dance attendees' heights has a cluster at the low end, which probably represents most of the children, and another cluster at the high end, which probably represents most of the adults. The range of the dance attendees is 2.5 feet, while the range of heights for the girl gymnasts is 1.75 feet and the range of heights for the boy basketball players is 1.5 feet. The distribution of dance attendees shows most variability.

16. The gymnasts should have a median close to 4.5 since that is about the middle of the data, and a mean at about the same location. The basketball players have a median of about 5.75 feet because that is about the middle of the data, and a mean at about the same location. The mean of the dance attendees will be between 5 and 5.5 feet because this appears to be where the balance point for the data is located. The median is at about the same place. The distribution is quite symmetrical and both mean and median will be in the middle. Notice very few people have the mean or median height for dance attendees.

© Pearson Education, Inc., publishing as Pearson Prentice Hall. All rights reserved.

**187**